Gatehouse

FRONTISPIECE: *Begun in 1860, the Gatehouse was to become the Hospital's virtual trademark, while neighborhood children thought it the home of Hansel and Gretel! Architect: Thomas & Dixon. Builder: John L. Gittier.*

Gatehouse

THE EVOLUTION
OF THE SHEPPARD
AND ENOCH PRATT
HOSPITAL, 1853-1986

BLISS FORBUSH
BYRON FORBUSH

Foreword by Robert W. Gibson, MD

THE SHEPPARD & ENOCH PRATT HOSPITAL • BALTIMORE, MARYLAND • 1986

FOR THIS BOOK:

EDITOR:
Winnie Perilla

ADDITIONAL TEXT & CAPTIONS:
Winnie Perilla

DESIGNER:
Timothy Nichols

PICTURE EDITORS:
Timothy Nichols
Winnie Perilla
Paul Preziosi

DESIGN ASSISTANT:
Mark Hodkin

TYPOGRAPHY:
Jill Hoen

PRINTED BY:
French/Bray, Inc.
Glen Burnie, MD, USA

PUBLISHER:
The Sheppard and Enoch Pratt Hospital
Baltimore, MD, USA

Dedication

To JOHN A. LUETKEMEYER, whose financial acumen, broad foresight and untiring energies have brought Sheppard Pratt to its present vanguard position as a comprehensive mental health center for treatment, education and research.

JOHN A. LUETKEMEYER: *Trustee 1953-1986; Vice President of the Board 1958-1972; President of the Board 1972-1985; Founding Member of the Trustees of the Education Center of Sheppard Pratt 1985—.*

Contents

Foreward

SINCE BLISS FORBUSH completed his original edition of the history of The Sheppard and Enoch Pratt Hospital 16 years ago, countless people have driven in and out of our Charles Street Gatehouse. And during that time many of those entering our campus have witnessed the construction of the new Central Building and the addition of the south wing of the Chapman Building. To the casual visitor, the most visible signs of change at Sheppard Pratt have been the myriad activities of bricklayers, carpenters and electricians.

Yet many more important changes are not so easily recognized. With the expansion of our inpatient services to include an Adolescent Short Term Unit and and Adult Intermediate Care Center, along with the constant growth of outpatient programs offered on campus, every year more and more people enter Sheppard Pratt through our Gatehouse.

And conversely, with the expansion of our community-based and education programs, every year more of the services offered by the Hospital have moved *outside* our Gatehouse to reach an even broader population. Soon, with the construction of the Education Center, our services will again be expanded to include a national center for behavioral studies and education.

The changes of the last 16 years have brought us to the threshold of a new era in mental health care provision. Under the leadership of Board of Trustees President Emeritus John D. Luetkemeyer, Sheppard

Pratt has been transformed from an institution with a limited range of clinical programs (all of which were clinical and half of which were custodial), into a comprehensive center for treatment, education and research.

Just as construction of Chapman South was an outward expression of change at Sheppard Pratt, so, too, construction of the Education Center will now serve to mirror the evolution of psychiatry's focus in the United States. We have reached the time when mental illness is no longer perceived as a stigma or mystery, but rather as an illness that can be arrested and treated.

As we enter into this new period we feel compelled to share with you the history that is Sheppard Pratt; the story that has brought us to our present threshold. To Bliss Forbush's original work, his son Byron has added the most recent chapters of our story from 1971 to the present. Around this text we have wrapped our 133-year story with a rich pictorial selection.

So as you enter this other *Gatehouse*, we hope that through these pages you, too, will take part in the rich tradition that is the "family" of Sheppard Pratt.

Robert W. Gibson, MD
President and Chief Executive Officer

Baltimore, May 1986

ABOVE: *The main towers of the A and B Buildings. One of the major efforts of the "Gibson era" was the construction of a new Central Building connecting the two original structures.*

Preface to the First Edition

FOR 80 YEARS The Sheppard and Enoch Pratt Hospital has provided sympathetic and skillful care to thousands of patients. It was founded by Moses Sheppard, a Quaker merchant of Baltimore, who desired that his estate be used for an experimental institution where the ratio of cures among the mentally disturbed might be increased. "I wish everything done for the comfort of the patient," Sheppard wrote, "to combine every feature that science and experience might indicate as requisite or desirable to minister to the greatest possible advantage to the patient."

A conservative business man, Moses Sheppard directed the Trustees to spend only the interest on the original principal as well as subsequent funds received. Thus, for nearly 30 years the Hospital had no patients; rather the Trustees were occupied with the purchase of land, planting trees and shrubbery, and constructing the main buildings. The first patient was not admitted until December 6, 1891.

The institution had been in operation for five years when Enoch Pratt, another Baltimore philanthropist, left a million dollars to extend the activities of the Sheppard Trust. His only stipulation was that the name be changed from the Sheppard Asylum to The Sheppard and Enoch Pratt Hospital.

Over the years, to doctors, nurses, attendants, administrative officers and maintenance workers, have been added occupational and recreational therapists, social workers, psychologists, secretaries, and a financial staff large enough to manage a seven million dollar annual budget. New buildings have been constructed to carry forward the wishes of Enoch Pratt. And without diminishing the three major lines of activities — care of patients, research, and teaching — vital community services have been added in recent years, extending the skills of the Hospital to colleges, training schools, general hospitals, and county clinics.

Hundreds of professionals have spent perhaps the finest years of their careers at Sheppard Pratt, seeking to provide the best possible care for the troubled, the anxious, the hysterical, the manic, the depressed, and in recent years, adolescents who suffer from drug abuse. Unfortunately only a few of the many with keen minds and tender hearts could be mentioned in this story. Through their outstanding efforts, many individuals have been able to return to home and society — renewed inwardly and outwardly. For those in whom this was impossible, life was at the very least made easier and more tolerable.

The research behind this story of The Sheppard and Enoch Pratt Hospital rests on thousands of pages of reports, minutes of meetings, essays, reprints, letters, and newspaper accounts preserved in the Hospital files. It notes changes in the development of psychiatry, administration, research, and teaching. Above all, it traces the progression of American society's ever-growing readiness to accept and treat mental illness.

My special appreciation goes to all those on the staff and those associated with the Hospital who not only worked to locate hard-to-find papers, early records and reprints, but also donated considerable time and thought in reading the manuscript. I am grateful to Ann Farquhar Forbush, whose literary skills have made the book more readable, and especially to my wife, LaVerne Hill Forbush, who had the tedious task of making corrections and giving suggestions for improvement on chapter after chapter and draft after draft.

Dr. Bliss Forbush
November 20, 1970

LEFT: *Dr. Bliss Forbush, author of the original text of this book (1971), and former President of Sheppard Pratt's Board of Trustees. Dr. Forbush was succeeded as Headmaster of Friends School in Baltimore by his son Byron, who currently serves on the Hospital Board.*

BELOW: *Artwork by Aaron Sopher, from the dust cover of the First Edition. In 1969 Sopher was commissioned to produce over 100 sketches of life at Sheppard Pratt; in 1970 many were sold to raise money for the Hospital. Sopher worked in pen-and-ink, occasionally coloring his sketches with tints made out of very strong coffee. Additional examples of Sopher's Sheppard Pratt work appear in the later chapters of this volume.*

1. Implementing the Founder's Plan

THE SHEPPARD and Enoch Pratt Hospital is representative of the indispensable contributions that private foundations have made to the growth and development of American psychiatry.

Before the 19th century, public institutions for the insane began in the workhouse, almshouse or jail, the only places where the indigent insane or untractable individual could be placed. The first public asylum in the United States "For Persons of Insane or Disordered Minds" was established at Williamsburg, Virginia, in 1773. Others followed in Maryland, in 1798, in Kentucky, 1824, in New York, 1825, in South Carolina, 1828, and in Worchester, Massachusetts, in 1833. These institutions were receptacles for the insane, places of refuge for the mentally disordered. Only as many decades passed did they become creditable mental hospitals.

The first hospital to make such provisions was the Pennsylvania Hospital, founded in 1751, for treating the insane. New York Hospital, opened in 1791, provided segregated areas for the mentally disordered. The blend of humanitarianism and scientific optimism that marked the first half of the 19th century was responsible for the establishment of other private asylums: the Friends Retreat at Frankford, Pennsylvania, in 1817; the McLean Asylum in Boston, in 1818; and the Hartford Retreat in Connecticut, in 1824. These private institutions provided a certain amount of experimentation, since they were supported in part by endowments and were not as restricted in their expenditures as the public institutions were compelled to be; nor were they flooded with more admissions than could be accommodated. Superintendents of both public and private asylums endeavored to practice humane and rational methods in the care of the insane.

The Sheppard and Enoch Pratt Hospital, chartered in 1853 but not opened to receive patients until 1891,

grew to a place of prominence among the privately endowed mental institutions of the East. Profiting greatly from the experience of those earlier institutions, Sheppard Pratt's program and treatment of patients reflects the development of psychiatry. Outstanding in Sheppard Pratt's history were two Medical Superintendents, Edward N. Brush and Ross Mc. Chapman, who both became Presidents of the American Psychiatric Association. Harry Stack Sullivan performed his major clinical research within its walls. Valuable papers included in standard psychiatric literature were written there, and three doctors from the Hospital staff became editors of psychiatric journals. As farsighted as Moses Sheppard was in founding an institution "to carry forward and improve the ameliorated system of treatment of the insane," he little dreamed that the contribution of his institution to psychiatry would be so extensive and far reaching.

Moses Sheppard, as a thoughtful member of the Religious Society of Friends, had a lifetime interest in what, at a later date, would be called "social causes." His religious motivation found expression in practical accomplishments. He was a warden of the city poor and a commissioner of the prison. Living in a period of ferment over slavery, he actively assisted freed Negroes of Maryland to migrate to Africa. When Moses Sheppard died in 1857 at the age of 82, he was familiar with the need for treatment of the mentally ill.

At the time, tragic conditions found in Maryland institutions for the mentally deranged were neither better nor worse than in most of the United States. Affluent families might employ an attendant for an afflicted member; if the invalid was a danger to himself or others, a cage for his confinement located in the attic or basement was often constructed. Managing a delusional, delirious, or overly aggres-

ABOVE: *Moses Sheppard, the Founder,*
whose Quaker upbringing led to a lifetime of
championing social causes.

sive individual in the home, however, proved almost impossible. In some instances the demented person wandered away, sleeping in a barn or haystack. Set upon by dogs, he was often the butt of cruel jokes by adolescents. His only other alternative was the local almshouse or jail.

Prior to the Civil War most insane persons were held in almshouses, where treatment was atrocious. Men and women were crowded into narrow cells, where, stripped of every comfort, they often were chained to the floor or to a staple driven into the wall. Food was coarse; little fresh air or sunlight reached the deranged, who lay on straw or on the damp floor. Many who might have been cured by timely treatment were transformed into raving maniacs. And so the almshouses or jails became the last resting place of living maniacs. Forgotten by their friends, they were neglected and abused by their keepers — often coarse and brutal men — whose function was solely custodial.

The first movement toward the moral and humane treatment of the mentally ill was instituted by Philippe Pinel in France and William Tuke in York, England. In place of floggings these men substituted kindness and sympathy. If necessary, leather straps were used to restrain arms and ankles of the violent patients. Noxious drugs, bleeding and blisterings, which marked past treatment, were replaced by warm baths, liberal diets, suitable amusements, and employment. An ordered schedule of activities was instituted. At the Retreat in York, there was a library; and patients were allowed to take pleasant walks in beautiful gardens. Religious services were provided. Attendants were trained to be gentle and courteous, though firm when necessary.

Several American institutions adopted the humane treatment instituted by Pinel and Tuke. Moses Sheppard was familiar with the Friends Retreat at Frankford, the Pennsylvania Hospital, the Bloomingdale Hospital in New York, and the McLean Asylum, all of which were proving grounds for these new methods of care.

In the winter of 1851-1852 Dorothea Lynde Dix, already well known for her crusade to improve conditions for the mentally ill, came to Baltimore and interested Moses Sheppard in her efforts to induce the Maryland Legislature to establish a new state institution for the care of the insane. The success of her work quickened Sheppard's desire to found an asylum free from any political domination or control to serve the Quakers of Maryland and as many of the general public as could be accommodated. In the spring of 1853 the Founder commissioned David M. Perine, for many years Registrar of Wills in Baltimore, to secure a charter from the General Assmebly for the asylum. The Act of Incorporation was presented to the House of Delegates, read and approved May 24, 1853, and given final approval by the Senate on May 28, 1853.

The first Trustees named were Moses Sheppard, David M. Perine, Dr. William Riley, Archibald Stirling, Charles Howard, William M. Metcalfe, and Richard H. Townsend. The Charter stated "that the object and design of the said Corporation is hereby declared to be, the founding and maintaining an Asylum for the insane; the entire management of which shall be vested in the said Trustees."

Having secured the permanence and safety of his proposed asylum, Sheppard called the first meeting of the Board. Five of the Trustees were Quakers, one a Presbyterian, and one an Episcopalian. One member was President of a railroad, one President of a Baltimore bank, two were bank directors, one a well known lawyer, one a physician, and one a business man associated with a large manufacturing firm. Sheppard was elected President and Townsend

was named Secretary. Few meetings were held in the following three years, although the Founder did write a list of guiding directives.

In these directives Sheppard wrote that the asylum was to care, "First, for the poor of the Society of Friends; secondly, for such of the Society as are able to pay, and then for the poor indiscriminately; afterwards the Trustees will use their discretion." When the time came for building, Sheppard declared that "courteous treatment and the comfort of all patients" be given first consideration in the plans for the grounds, buildings, and medical care. Remembering the shackled inmates he had observed in the damp basements of several almshouses, he directed that no patient should be confined below ground and that all should have privacy with ample sunlight and fresh air. He was of the opinion that the rate of cures might be increasd if the new buildings resembled a private residence, both inside and out.

J. Saurin Norris often quoted Moses Sheppard's injunction, "Put first the comfort of the patient." But Gerard Reese remarked that such a new institution might soon be filled with deranged individuals who could not be cured, but who would live on year after year, filling the asylum. The Founder replied that he hoped to establish a *curative* institution, stating that in the future an incurable patient was to be removed to make room for another who might be restored to reason.

This Quaker humanitarian had two further requests for his fellow Trustees to consider. One, that in the new asylum they would "combine every feature that science and experience might indicate as requisite or desirable to minister to the greatest possible advantage of the patients." The other, that the Trustees would bear in mind "that it is the income, not the principal of the Estate, that is to sustain the Institution." This rather unusual stipulation delayed the opening of the Sheppard Asylum for several decades and made the governing body the target of some abuse. But in the long run these guidelines enabled the seven men to construct a set of beautiful and well-equipped buildings, to carry forward a large program of benevolences, and to provide funds for future development.

Moses Sheppard died on the first of February 1857, at his home on Pratt Street, Baltimore. His house became the headquarters of the Trustees for many years. The Board, now presided over by J. Saurin Norris, was left Sheppard's entire estate, including his house, furnishings, books, and papers. By the following spring Norris reported that their inheritance was $571,440.41. Up to that time, this was the largest single bequest made to any mental institution in America.

A search was immediately begun for a suitable locaton for the future asylum, and after inspecting many locations, a 340 acre farm known as Mt. Airy, six miles from Baltimore on the York Road, was purchased for $60,000. In order to connect with the recently extended Charles Street, an additional 35 acres were acquired. The first year was spent securing topographical surveys of the property; selecting sites for future buildings; planning roads; and, with the aid of a landscape gardener, planting ornamental trees and shrubs. These trees, which grew to majestic heights during the next hundred years, were mostly elm, beach, maple, hemlock and pine. As the farm was expected to supply future patients with fruits and vegetables, 334 fruit trees were planted; fields were limed and fertilized.

A Baltimore firm, Thomas and James M. Dixon, won a $300 prize for the best of 21 designs submitted for the main building. Because of his recent services as Superintendent of the newly constructed Bloomingdale Hospital at White Plains, New York,

LEFT: *Antique English cellarette in the Adam style, circa 1770, belonging to Moses Sheppard. As a Quaker, Sheppard was nominally a teetotaler, so one may assume the liquor contained herein was reserved for guests. In any event, Sheppard kept his alcohol out of sight!*

third place winner Dr. D. Tilden Brown was chosen as chief consultant. Calvert Vaux, who had already designed New York City's Central Park, was named associate architect. While the architect was making preliminary studies, Brown was sent to England and France to obtain ideas that might prove helpful to the building of Sheppard. Anything suggestive of a prison-like appearance was to be avoided. The buildings were to be fireproof as far as possible, and to feature many windows.

As the building plans developed, they closely followed the design suggested by Dr. Robert Kirkbride of the Pennsylvania Hospital, which were published in the *Journal of Insanity* and had been studied by the Founder. Kirkbride advocated an asylum of 250 patients, the most he thought a medical superintendent could adequately supervise. He recommended a central building with wings providing ample accommodations for reception rooms, bedrooms, parlors, a library, lecture rooms, a chapel, kitchen, dining rooms, and quarters for the medical staff and other employees. Designed to house 15 patients with attendants, each wing or ward was to contain work rooms, reading rooms, and sun porches. He suggested that certain rooms to be used by excitable patients have doors with heavily glazed glass windows to allow close observation. For construction, Kirkbride recommended that walls be 18 inches thick in order to enclose flues that would carry heat and fresh air. Floors should rest on brick arches, with stone used in kitchens and wash rooms; stairways should be of iron, and roofs of slate.

Following Kirkbride's general ideas, the Trustees decided to construct two buildings, each 360 feet long. One was designated for men and the other for women. Identical in every detail, they were placed in a line with each other, 100 feet apart. In May 1860 a contract was let for the erection of an Entrance and Lodge to be built on the Charles Street side. This charming building, resembling a Swiss chalet, became a trademark of Sheppard and a delight to passersby. To the neighborhood children, it was the home of Hansel and Gretel.

Finding on the property an excellent quality of brick clay, the contractors constructed two kilns, each holding 60,000 units. A contract was let for a million bricks at $6.00 per thousand. On another portion of the farm, a quarry was opened, from which stone was cut to be used in foundations and stairways. A pair of oxen was purchased to haul bricks and stone to the construction site.

In May of 1861 work was delayed due "to the extraordinary revulsions which have taken place in the community." A Baltimore mob had fired upon the Sixth Massachusetts Regiment passing through on its way to Washington. Railroad service between the North and the Capital was disrupted by the transportation of soldiers and supplies so that powder could not be secured for blasting in the quarry. It was only the prelude to four bloody years of Civil War.

Ground was broken, however, for the Western Division of the Hospital on May 25, 1862; a start was made on building a barn, stables, granaries, carriage and wagon sheds, a shop for repairs, and several farm houses. Some 300 feet south of the main buildings, a power plant and laundry were constructed. This building was connected with the Western Division by a subway to accommodate heating and water pipes and, later, electric lines.

In spite of wartime conditions, work went steadily forward on the Western Division. Foundations were laid, iron beams erected to support the arches, and walls carried upward. The ground floor of each section contained 75 rooms, which were used for kitchens, dining rooms, patient activities, and storage.

LEFT: Moses Sheppard's covered bidet, probably of American origin, circa 1820.
BELOW: Polychrome English political cartoons belonging to Moses Sheppard, and part of a considerable collection of such items dating from the 1820s and 30s. Sheppard amassed a large number of such works, most of which still remain uncatalogued. Although he probably purchased them for pennies in the mid-19th Century, their value in today's market is considerable.

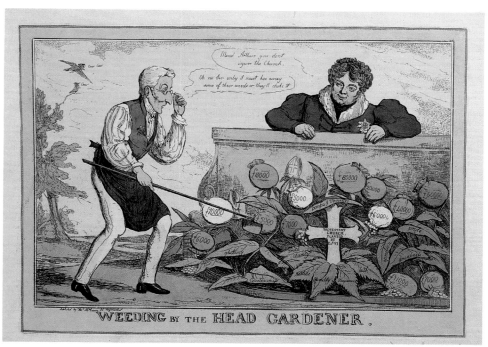

WEEDING BY THE HEAD GARDENER.

CATHOLIC ASCENDENCY. or St Patrick's Day in the Morning

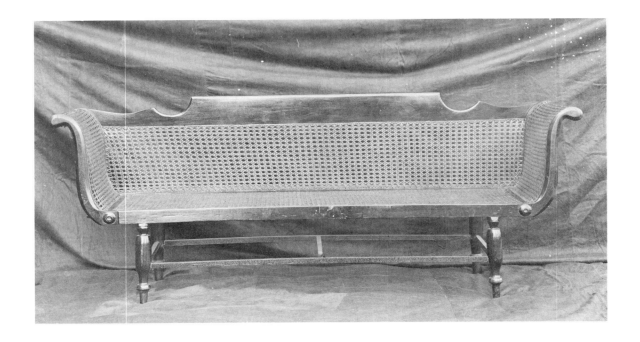

TOP: *A caned sofa made in Liberia and sent to Moses Sheppard in gratitude for putting its donor through university and medical school in the United States.*
ABOVE: *Moses Sheppard's telescope, which has long resided in Overlook, home of the Hospital's Medical Directors.*

Main offices and reception rooms were located at each end of the divisions facing one another. Whereas, in the old almshouses, the sick-poor, orphaned-poor, aged-poor, mentally disturbed, retarded and idiots had been housed together; the new system fostered the beginnings of psychiatric classification. The most disturbed patients were placed in the wing farthest removed from the offices, with the less disturbed patients next, and convalescent individuals closest to the reception rooms and library. The second floor duplicated the first, and the third floor and smaller fourth floor were reserved for nurses and other employees. In each division there were approximately 50 rooms on the two top floors. Patient bedrooms averaged 10 by 14 feet, the parlors 18 by 32 feet, and the sunrooms 8 by 20 feet. Corridors were 10 feet wide. The entire length of the two divisions, counting the central open space, was 820 feet.

Year by year the buildings rose higher, the Trustees expending only the interest on their capital. The quality of workmanship and materials used was of the best. The entire Western Division was under roof by 1871 and excavation for the Eastern Division began immediately. By 1880, all the brick work required at the asylum had been completed. Burning the eleven million bricks used in construction took several decades. The soft red bricks baked on the grounds gave a pleasing exterior to the structures. Each was topped by a six-story tower ending in a wedge and encircled by a lattice-work balcony. Where the divisions faced each other wide porches made the edifice look home-like; the long walls of the wings were broken by charming oriel windows, and a secondary tower of more modest design. The effect was of a pleasing Victorian establishment.

To the public, not knowing the restrictions in Sheppard's will, the construction seemed to pro-

BELOW: Examples of the working drawings
for A Building, made circa 1854. In the days
before blueprints, such drawings were
copied and colored entirely by hand.

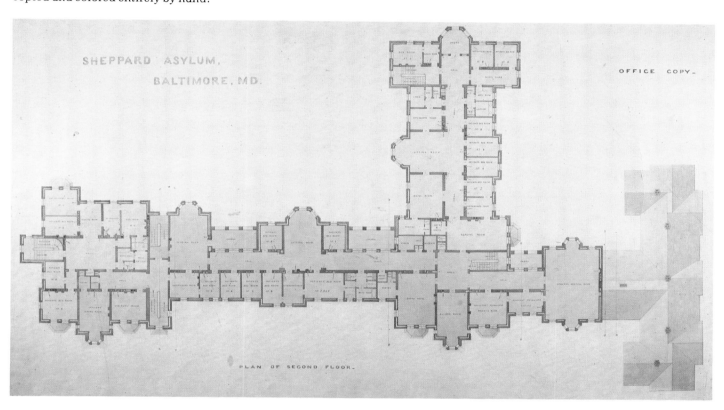

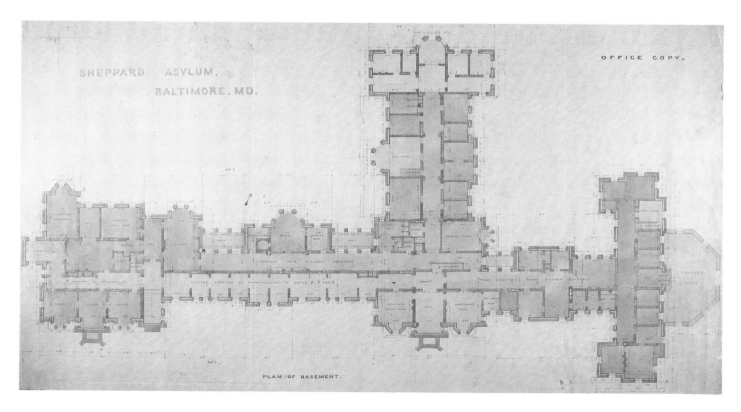

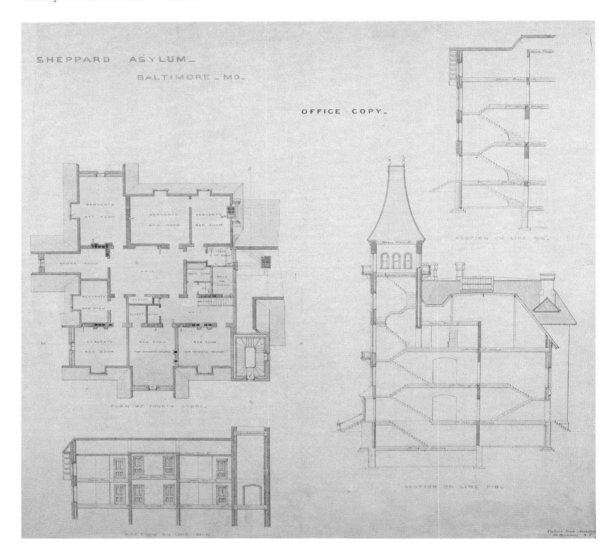

RIGHT: *Another of Moses Sheppard's English polychrome political cartoons.*
BELOW: *Original plans for the floor and elevation of the A Building Tower. Like the others on the preceeding pages, this was a pen-and-ink, hand-colored working drawing from the days before blueprints.*
OPPOSITE TOP: *A panorama of the A and B Buildings, taken circa 1910 presumably from a treetop near Norris Cottage.*
OPPOSITE BOTTOM: *Moses Sheppard's shaving stand, part of the Founder's collection of memorabilia in Overlook.*

ceed very slowly. A local proverb developed which Baltimoreans used when they wished to postpone any task: ''When the Sheppard is finished, I'll do it.'' The Trustees refused to spend more than the annual interest and though at times it was necessary to borrow against their securities to complete some yearly project, the original bequest remained intact.

In 1891, when the asylum was ready to admit the first patient, the Trustees had expended on the farm and building operations a sum larger than the amount originally inherited from the Founder! On construction, the following amounts were spent:

1860	$ 6,923.11
1865	131,412.74
1870	313,035.34
1875	479,559.32
1880	603,901.13
1885	713,935.12
1890	881,262.27

In 1890 the total assets of the Corporation amounted to $1,471,779.47.

Joseph Camp, who supervised the construction from the beginning, lived to see the work accomplished; and an unnamed bricklayer who laid the cornerstone of the Western Division put the final brick on the last chimney of the Eastern Division. David Perine, who had drawn up the charter, resigned from the Trustees in his eighty-second year in 1878. The greatest loss, however, was the death of John Saurin Norris. Picked by Moses Sheppard as the second President, he had guided the Corporation through the 22 years during which the undertaking was launched.

2. The First Decade

AS THE TIME drew near for opening the Asylum, the Trustees adopted by-laws and established the Finance, Asylum, and Farm Committees. After interviewing Superintendents of several mental institutions, the Trustees offered the position of Physician-in-Chief and Superintendent to Edward N. Brush, MD, then Assistant Superintendent of the Pennsylvania Hospital for the Insane.

The new Superintendent appointed as his associates Dr. L. Gibbons Smart, an assistant physician at The Johns Hopkins Medical School, and Mrs. Caroline R. Wright, a graduate of the Bellevue Hospital Training School, as his first Superintendent of Nurses.

With senior staffing well in hand, the Board compiled a set of admission requirements. For financial security, the Board required a bond signed by two parties for each entering patient. Payment was due in advance for a three-month period, and a deposit to cover incidental expenses and possible damage to asylum equipment was required. A medical statement from physicians indicating the need for treatment was requested. It was hoped that applicants would voluntarily apply for admission, but actually the majority were placed in the asylum on doctors' certificates. A publication of the Sheppard, the *Announcement*, mentioned that, "Patients should never be brought to the Asylum by deception, they almost always suspect the deception, and it invariably has a bad effect more or less permanent. They learn on arrival that the Sheppard is not a hotel or watering place, and are very apt to feel that the medical officer and others connected with the institution are parties to the deception, and decline to give them their confidence, so necessary to the successful dealing with their cases."

On December 6, 1891 the first patient was received. She was a 46 year old single woman with the simple diagnosis of dementia. Almost no information exists about her background except a note that she had suffered an attack of neurasthenia of short duration in 1866, at which time she was described as cataleptic. The illness that brought her to the Sheppard was said to have started 15 years before. A few weeks after the asylum opened, a young man was admitted who apparently was troubled by lack of memory and increasing confusion. With a long history of antisocial behavior and irritability, he had threatened actions against members of his family. From a well-to-do family, he had been barred from his home and his clubs because "his wild life of gaiety led to embarrassment of his friends and family." His case is of special interest, because after the young man was committed, some of his well-meaning friends declared the young man had been confined illegally and were able to secure his premature release. His dissolute life continued, and he was returned to the Sheppard a few weeks later.

The Superintendent reported that during the first full year, 1892, the average number of patients under care was 20. There were 53 admissions and 27 discharges. Of these patients, four recovered, three were much improved, and six improved; four died. Improvement of patients was credited to a satisfactory environmental adjustment including outdoor walks, work, and games. A balanced diet and plenty of sleep were scheduled. A minimum of restraints, such as chair straps and wet sheet packs, were employed. Morphine and its derivatives were regarded as useful drugs; tonics were administered in some cases, mustard and salt baths were valuable. According to the Superintendent's reports, occasionally stramonium was used in the case of mania, and digitalis or conium in cases of melancholia. Chloral hydrate, the first of the synthetically produced sedatives, was helpful. Sodium amytal, one of the

RIGHT: *A carriage arriving at the entrance to A Building, circa 1900.*
BELOW: *The Physician-in-Chief, Dr. Edward N. Brush. From a portrait painted by Thomas C. Corner in 1917.*

most valuable of the newly discovered barbiturates, proved useful in treatment. An orderly system of classification of patients was established, and a beginning was made in recording case histories.

The first case that made possible legal action against the institution involved a woman who committed suicide. The husband accused the asylum of negligence and asked the Trustees to indemnify his children for the loss of their mother. After carefully considering the case, Mr. Joseph Grape, Secretary to the Board, wrote that since the charter clearly outlined the duties of the Trustees, and the Founder had given careful instructions concerning the use of his funds, the Board had no authority to devote any of the estate for the purpose requested. Their duty had been discharged, the Board declared, when they selected a competent Physician-in-Chief who in turn appointed a well-trained staff to have charge of the patients. "It is well known," Grape added for the Trustees, "that insane people...possess abnormal cunning...and they outwit the most wonderful care that experienced foresight can devise, short of cruel restraints." The husband did not pursue the matter.

With each new patient, Brush remained a strong advocate of voluntary admissions. Whenever an individual was able to comprehend his disordered condition and realize that treatment could be secured at the Sheppard, voluntary admission was in order. If a voluntary patient requested release and secured staff consent, the family was notified and the patient discharged in three days. If the staff could not approve of release, the family was asked to secure legal commitment. Often those who were mentally ill withdrew their request for release after consulting with the staff. Convalescent patients were at liberty to come and go at will within the asylum grounds.

Yet, the practice of voluntary release was not without damaging effects for some patients. Cures that the

TOP: *The Medical Staff of 1903. Standing: Drs. S.W. Ludlum, W.R. Dunton, Mr. Stewart Payton, Dr. Glanville Rusk. Sitting: Dr. E.N. Brush, Dr. Charles N. Franklin.* **ABOVE:** *In the days before oil heating there was coal. The task of the workman shown was to fill the large coal hoppers which fed the mechanical furnace stokers. The large tubes beneath the hoppers housed turning screws which moved a continuous supply of fresh coal onto the fire grates.*

RIGHT: *One of the steam-driven generators in the Powerplant, as it was in 1906. The huge leather belts drove the generators, whose distribution panels may been seen to the rear of the photograph.*
BELOW: *The Solarium, seen in 1905. Indoor tropical plant "winter gardens" were very popular at the time, and at the Hospital doubtless served to keep a goodly number of patients occupied with their upkeep.*

TOP: *Fordham, formerly Poe Cottage, photographed in 1921. Built by a wealthy Southern family for their daughter's private residence, Poe Cottage served this role for nearly forty years while the woman was a patient at Sheppard Pratt! Note the duckboard walkways, ubiquitous in the days before paved sidewalks.*
ABOVE: *An example of an individual tray service for patients, circa 1915, and fully commensurate with what a deluxe hotel of the time would offer its guests.*
RIGHT: *Norris Cottage, named for the second President of the Board, was originally equipped to take four patients and their attendants. Dr. Brush felt that some patients might benefit from being placed in smaller units.*

LEFT: *The fall of 1906: an increasing number of newfangled horseless carriages begin to find their way through the Gatehouse on Charles Street and up to the Hospital on the Hill. This example is parked in front of A Building, with B Building in the background.*

BELOW: *The Alcove of A Building. The room to the left was Dr. Brush's library, afterwards used as a medical library and later given over to stenographers. The room to the right was used as a staff dining room until 1908, when it, too, was taken over by the Hospital's growing stenographic staff.*

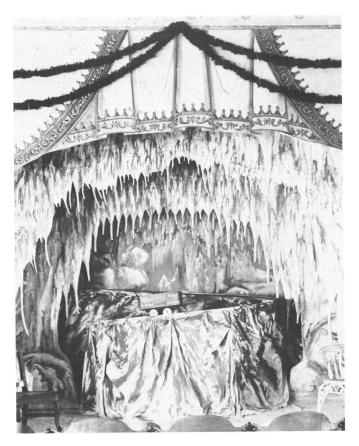

RIGHT: *A papier-mache ice cave, part of the Hospital's Christmas decorations for 1898, presumably constructed by the patients.*
FAR RIGHT: *An example of the "Light Swedish gymnastics" instituted by Dr. Brush just after the turn of the century. Here a nurse is handling the coaching chores for a group of male patients.*

staff was eager to accomplish were sometimes nullified by premature removal. There was the natural desire of the family to take the convalescent out of the asylum as soon as possible, often at the repeated request of the patient who longed to return home. Frequently the patient did not realize how dependent he was on continuous treatment. In some cases, early removal jeopardized or destroyed the likelihood of a permanent cure. In a number of other unfortunate cases, early removal against medical advice was followed by suicide.

A few alcoholics and opium addicts were admitted, often without the staff being fully informed of their condition. Sadly, Brush did not believe such individuals were curable. One patient who was admitted in an excitable condition was proved to be feigning insanity, although the files do not explain such an unusual procedure.

The daily average of patients steadily increased, reaching nearly 100 at the end of ten years. Of the patients admitted during those first ten years, 390 were married, 387 single, 89 widowed, and eight divorced. The first 874 patients admitted into the Sheppard came from 28 states and the District of Columbia. In that decade, of this first group of patients, 752 were judged insane. When discharged, 168 were recorded as cured, 111 much improved, 120 improved, and 172 unimproved. Of those patients discharged as recovered, the records indicate few relapses.

Always striving for an increased recovery rate, the Superintendent thought that some patients might profit from being placed in smaller units, as in the cottage system used at Bloomingdale Asylum. The Norris Cottage, a stone building on the York Road side, named for the second President of the Board, was equipped to take four patients and their attendants. Later, Fordham, or Poe Cottage, was built by a family for their daughter, who lived in it for 40 years.

Following the intentions of the Donor, Brush, too, had great sympathy for those who could not pay for the long treatment necessary in mental institutions. State and county institutions were available, although many counties in Maryland provided only almshouse care. In any case, it was necessary under the Maryland law to have an individual declared a pauper before the county or state institution would admit him. Thus Brush admitted a number of individuals at "rates far below what might be termed reasonable for the service rendered, and for a considerable period maintained others without charge." Such concessions were confined to persons living in Maryland with a hopeful prognosis. The Superintendent reported: "Some of these cases required more than usual attention, demanding by reason of their condition, special nursing and diet, and an amount of general and professional care that cannot be estimated in money value. All this has been ungrudgingly given and most satisfactory returns have been received in more than one instance." Among the first 752 cases, 52 were admitted free of charge, and only one-third of the patients paid the per capita cost.

According to the figures, charitable services rendered amounted in the first ten years to $211,357.47. The administration received from the Sheppard income $132,337.05 and from patients who paid more than the per capita cost, $78,042.42. For example, in 1901 it was necessary to draw on the income of the endowment fund to the amount of $29,000.00 in order to balance accounts.

Meanwhile, construction went forward on the unfinished Eastern Division. The Trustees reported to the Governor that by 1891 the value of their buildings and grounds was now $949,570.71, and the investments amounted to $568,827.44, a total of $1,518,398.71, "all derived from the bequest of the late Moses Sheppard."

Brush increased the recreational opportunities for the patients by adding a shuffleboard court and a small golf course. Light Swedish gymnastics were instituted; and efforts were made to secure outside entertainment in the form of lectures, musical programs, and discussion courses. Religious services were held Sunday afternoons. Brush reported a need for more books and magazines for the library, stating that the addition of a general assembly or lecture hall was desirable. He hoped that some day a hydrotherapy system could be installed.

During the first ten years of operation, 874 patients were treated for mental disturbances, diagnosed as follows:

DIAGNOSIS	MEN	WOMEN	TOTAL	DIAGNOSIS	MEN	WOMEN	TOTAL
Melancholia	86	81	167	Paresis	55	3	58
Confusional	18	17	35	Dementia	36	22	58
Hypochon-				Following			
driacal	13	3	16	apoplexy	4	1	5
Melancholia,				Epileptic	2	1	3
Chronic	18	29	47	Senile	10	5	15
Hypochon-				Imbecility, with			
drical	8	0	8	disturbance	7	8	15
Recurrent	3	12	15	Not insane,			
Senile	1	5	6	Alcoholism	3	0	3
Mania, acute	38	39	77	Aphasis	0	2	2
Acute delirious	3	0	3	Choree	0	1	1
Confusional	17	7	24	Delirium	1	1	2
Following				Cocaine habit	1	1	2
Bright's disease	1	0	1	Epilepsy	0	1	1
Postoperative	0	3	3	Feigned insanity	1	0	1
Puerperal	0	8	8	Hypochrondriasis	1	0	1
Subacute	10	13	23	Hysteria	0	6	6
Mania, chronic	22	43	65	Inebriety	74	3	77
Chronic				Meningitis	1	0	1
delusional	0	12	12	Morphia and			
Circular	0	1	1	ocaine habit	6	1	7
Paranoia	43	21	64	Neurasthenia	7	4	11
Recurrent	8	14	22	Opium habit	3	5	8
				TOTALS	500	372	874

3. Enoch Pratt's Bequest

ENOCH PRATT, a wealthy Baltimore merchant, died on September 17, 1896, making the Trustees of the Sheppard Asylum his residuary legatee. Born in 1809 in North Middleborough, Massachusetts, he came to Baltimore in 1831, where he established a prosperous hardware firm. As his fortune accumulated, Enoch Pratt developed many business interests, becoming a director of banks, railroads, and steamship companies. Several of Pratt's social and business connections brought him in contact with Moses Sheppard, whose humanitarian considerations he shared.

Enoch Pratt felt that the greatest need for the city of his adoption was a free circulating library open to all citizens regardless of race. He provided this through a gift to Baltimore of $1,058,333.00. But Pratt's charitable works were far from over. He became interested in the Sheppard Asylum through a request for advice concerning some investments, visited the institution a number of times, and talked to the Physician-in-Chief. Once he asked Dr. Brush for a brief statement of what the Asylum could accomplish if it had additional funds. The next time he saw the Superintendent, he said, "You need more money. You'll get it."

Records show that the philanthropist told Mr. Pope, then President of the Board, "that he had watched the course of the trustees and the conduct of the institution, and that the trustees had more closely adhered to the wishes of the Founder than any similar body of which he had knowledge."

The forthcoming bequest of Enoch Pratt amounted to $1,631,493.18, which, with the estate held by the Trustees now totaling $1,576,792.79, placed the institution in a very favorable position indeed. According to his will, Pratt stated that he did not want to alter the management of the asylum, but it was his wish "that the income from the residuary estate shall be used to complete the present buildings and grounds, and for the erection of such additional buildings as will accommodate not less than 200 additional inmates, and after that the income...be devoted to the indigent insane...*at very low rates*, or absolutely free, as the Trustees...may deem best and wisest..." The one condition attached to the bequest was to change the name of the corporation to "The Sheppard and Enoch Pratt Hospital." The Trustees accepted the new name, approved by the legislature in 1898.

Brush welcomed the substitution of the name *hospital* for *asylum*, which to him suggested a new era in psychiatry. The concept of an asylum that existed in the days of Moses Sheppard suggested a place of refuge where the mentally ill could escape from the neglect, cruelty, and mistreatment endured in attic or cellar, almshouse or jail. The word *Retreat* as used by the Friends in their foundation at Frankford, or the medical group in Connecticut in establishing the Hartford Retreat, suggested a place of shelter away from the world, of custodial nature, where humane and gentle care would suffice to make the inmates comfortable, or a place where a man or woman approaching senility might retire in peace to continue his deterioration until released by death. It was more than fortuitous that Pratt asked that the name of the institution be changed, for an *asylum* was out of date. In changing the name of the Sheppard from *asylum* to *hospital*, the Trustees turned their backs on the past and pushed forward in a new direction. The new concept marked a change to a place where medical treatment, rather than custodial care, would be developed.

Brush declared, "Modern thought and practice in the care of the insane all point to the hospital idea, and if the general hospital may receive without question or doubt any and all who apply at its doors, it

ABOVE: *Enoch Pratt. Like Moses Sheppard,
Pratt was a philanthropist. Upon his death in
1896, the Hospital's Trustees found themselves
blessed with a $1.6 million bequest which came
with only one condition: the name of the
corporation was to be changed to include that
of its new benefactor.*

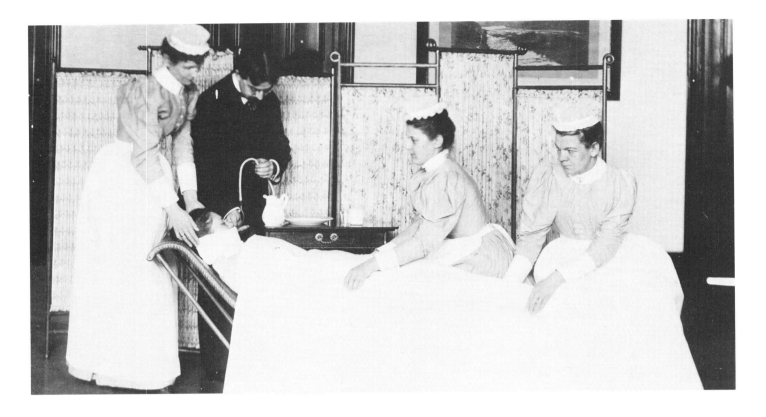

TOP: *This photograph illustrating oral feeding accompanied an article by Dr. Brush entitled "Hospital Treatment of the Insane."*
ABOVE: *The Medical Staff of 1911: Doctors Clarance B. Farrar, Sanger Brown, William R. Dunton, Jr., Edward N. Brush (Superintendent), and George F. Sargent.*

certainly seems in the line of progress to encourage voluntary application of patients at the doors of the special hospital,'' He added, ''The mentally unbalanced are sick, and in the earlier and recoverable stages of the disease, the physical disabilities are often as plainly distinguishable as the mental disturbances; indeed they are sometimes even more plainly recognizable.''

Brush looked forward to the time when the stigma attached in the public mind to mental illness would be removed, and individuals would come as freely to the mental as to the general hospital.

Although the Trustees were left ''unfettered to use the income, or the corpus, or both, for the purpose of the institution,'' they decided to preserve intact the corpus of this new estate. They recognized that by ''spending only the annual interest received they might not be able to benefit as many sufferers of the present generation, but such a practice would preserve their work for good as the years passed.''

Funds were set aside for increasing the size of the medical library, and 52 medical and psychiatric journals, published in the United States and seven foreign countries, were ordered. To carry on new research, it was necessary to pursue clinical and pathological studies, to have available a well-stocked medical library, and to enlarge the staff with well-trained specialists. A clinical and pathological laboratory was set up in the Western Division, with Dr. Stewart Paton, a well-trained neurologist and neuropathologist, as Director. Dr. Clarence B. Farrar, a graduate of The Johns Hopkins Medical School — later to become a well-known writer and editor in psychiatry — was appointed Clinical Assistant.

Soon articles written by members of the staff appeared in medical and psychiatric journals. Brush had already written a number of papers — such as ''Hysterical Insanity,'' ''Insanity and Arrested Devel-

opment," and "An Analysis of One Hundred Cases of Acute Melancholia." Later he wrote about hospital administration, producing "The Organization of Hospitals for the Insane," "Hospital Treatment of the Insane," and "Commitment and Detention of the Insane." Paton wrote on the study of patients in mental hospitals, the advances in medicine in relation to psychiatry, and technical subjects such as "The Histogenesis of the Cellular Elements of the Cerebral Cortex." Farrar produced studies of methods of psychiatry and several papers dealing with dementia praecox.

Despite this extensive research, as yet no formal program of psychiatric training for physicians existed. Thus, young doctors planning to continue their careers in mental hospitals or to enter private practice as psychiatrists came to Sheppard Pratt for postgraduate experience. Between 1898 and 1908, eight assistant physicians and eight clinical assistants were employed, few of whom remained for more than two years.

Throughout this period of psychiatric advancement, the responsibilities of the Medical Superintendent were extensive. According to the Book of Rules of the Hospital, he was expected to have a personal knowledge of every patient, to visit the wards every 24 hours, and to examine the daily reports of all physicians and nurses. He was required to supervise all the nonclinical operations of the Hospital, giving care to expenditures. It was his duty to observe the laws of Maryland regarding the admission and detention of patients, and to see that all medical records were properly kept. He was expected to report regularly to the Trustees, and to make written recommendations for the betterment of the institution. He was to be absent from the institution for more than a 12 hour period only with the consent of the President of the Board!

The assistant physicians were required to visit their assigned areas every morning and night, and more frequently if the condition of a patient required it. Each was carefully to note the condition of his patients, look after their diet, bathing, and cleanliness, and see that the ward was properly heated and ventilated. They were expected to associate freely with the patients, observing their idiosyncrasies, mental and physical conditions, and to aid in devising amusements, recreation, and employment. It was their duty to indicate where they could be found in emergencies, and two were always on duty. Thus the isolation of the Hospital, the confining duties, and the necessity of living-in were chiefly responsible for the all-too-rapid turnover among the assistant physicians.

The influence of the nursing staff could not be overestimated. As Brush indicated, no matter how well equipped the buildings were, or how competent and enthusiastic the medical staff, the comfort of the patients and the success with which they were managed depended largely on the Nursing Department. Such a staff was hard to find. No training school for nurses existed in general hospitals in America before 1872, and it was somewhat later, in 1882, that the first training school for psychiatric nurses was established at the McLean Hospital. Since properly trained psychiatric nurses were not widely available, a training school was established at Sheppard Pratt in 1905. A curriculum was planned to include instruction by the medical staff in physiology, anatomy, medical chemistry, hygiene, practical nursing, administration of medication and diet, care of the sick, and the meeting of emergencies. A highly qualified group of doctors and graduate nurses from the Medical Schools of Johns Hopkins and the University of Maryland supplemented the hard-pressed Sheppard Pratt staff.

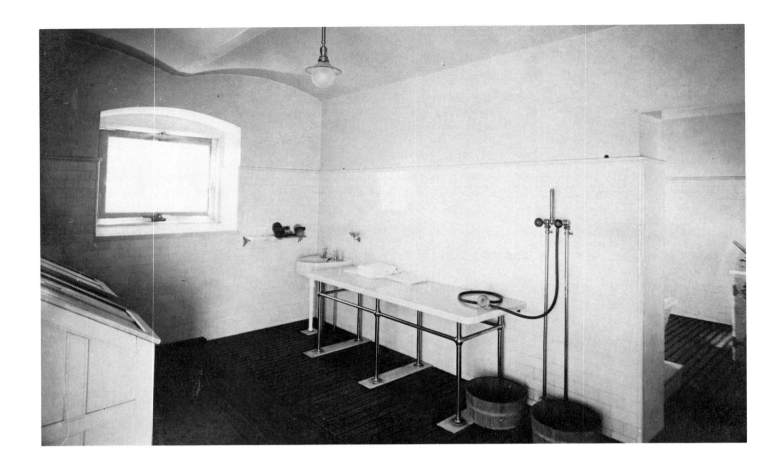

In one of his reports, Brush made the statement, "There is little mysterious or peculiar in the methods of study or treatment of insanity, or in the knowledge of its causes. We must first know what kind of brain and nervous system the patient has inherited, what conditions of bodily vigor he has had when in presumed mental health, and then we must know how he has used his inheritance. Many a man has been born into the world with a tendency toward physical or mental deterioration, who by careful use of his already impaired physical capital, has continued physically and mentally solvent throughout life, while his less fortunate neighbor, by ignorance and reckless use of his splendid physical endowment, has become bankrupt in life and mind and more than fortune."

To many, there seemed much that was mysterious surrounding insanity. Was insanity a brain disease? Was it related to the role of microorganisms? Were demonstrated metabolic disorders a cause of mental disorders? Were structural and physiological disturbances the basic factors? On an early trip to Scotland, Brush was greatly impressed when he observed the use of the thyroid gland of sheep in myxedema and cretinism. On his return to the Hospital, he instituted the thyroid treatment with certain patients whose cases seemed hopeless, and in a few cases there was remarkable improvement. A noisy, turbulent, destructive patient became quiet and manageable. A 40 year-old stenographer who was dull, listless, and unable to continue her work was given two grams of desiccated thyroid gland three times daily, and in a matter of months was able to resume her old position and keep steadily at work. Although other patients were similarly improved, there were cases where no benefit was secured, resulting in many disappointing failures. The Medical Superintendent felt that some cases of chronic mania, dementia,

and melancholia yielded to this new treatment, but he confessed ignorance of the resulting physiological action.

In 1902, when Brush returned from his second visit to mental institutions in Europe, he was even more enthusiastic about increased knowledge concerning the treatment and prevention of insanity. He saw outstanding new buildings, although in one case a hospital was so crowded that patients slept on the floor. He noted individuals on long bed-rest treatment who he thought would be better out of doors; he observed the prolonged use of baths to control overexcited patients. For the first time, he met a female physician serving on the ward of a mental hospital. He purchased a large microscope made in Jena at the Zeiss optical works and a machine to project microphotographs on a screen. On his return he was granted funds for enlarged quarters for the pathologial laboratory. Farrar was sent abroad to work in the laboratories at Heidelberg. At Sheppard Pratt, pathological analyses of autopsies were performed, and studies in the development, anatomy, and pathology of the central nervous system were made and published.

Physical improvement to the Hospital paralleled the advances made in education. After liquidating a debt of $53,000.00 accumulated in completing the Eastern Division, the Trustees agreed to use some of the income from the Pratt bequest for building expansions. In 1901 a ridge of land rising several hundred feet north of the main buildings was leveled so that a recreational casino could be constructed. A one-and-a-half story building, the Casino was surrounded on three sides by a 12½ foot veranda. In the basement, a two-lane bowling alley was built, with an adjacent room for billiards. The first floor contained a wide hall, large enough for light gymnastics, and space for looms, games, art work, sewing, read-

LEFT: *Hydrotherapy equipment consisted of a 22 foot square pool, a large lounge, and adjacent rooms containing steam cabinets, shampoo tables, a spray and rain bath, and large porcelain tubs for continuous baths.*
ABOVE: *The douche room was part of the hydrotherapy department. From 20 to 30 patients a day were treated with the soothing effects of hydrotherapy.*

ing and smoking. An open fireplace lent a cheerful air in cold weather. It was hoped that this building, "within convenient distance, and yet away from the main buildings, (would) allure the patients out of their rooms into the tonic of the fresh air." The Casino cost approximately $30,000.00.

The next major improvement was the addition of hydrotherapy apparatus. Placed in the western end of the Western Division, this equipment consisted of a 22 foot square pool, a large lounge, and adjacent rooms containing steam cabinets, shampoo tables, a spray and rain bath, and large porcelain tubs for continuous baths. Under the care of nurses specially trained to operate the equipment, the hydrotherapy establishment proved of great value, especially with overactive patients. Soon from 20 to 30 patients a day were being treated in this way.

It was always intended that the grounds should approach, as closely as possible, the appearance of a beautiful park. To develop a long-range plan, a landscape architect from Boston was employed to develop the layout, construct new walks and drives, and to plant shrubs and trees. Up until this time, water for Sheppard Pratt had been drawn from 30 springs, and the supply was collected and pumped to the buildings. Eventually this supply proved inadequate, and the first of several artesian wells was sunk, the first to a depth of 250 feet. The laundry was reconstructed at a cost of $30,000.00, and a new dairy barn was built.

Despite the building expansion, it became necessary to limit the number of admissions. Patients were admitted solely on the basis of their mental condition. Some families requested comfortable custodial care for elderly relatives or for a person mentally defective since childhood. These the Hospital did not admit. Now and then the staff decided with regret that "we have reached the limit of our

ability to receive excited and turbulent cases, without manifest injustice to those who are quiet and self-controlled among our patients." It was often difficult to judge admissions because of inability to obtain a correct, complete case history. The statement that an applicant was excited or depressed, confused or dull and feeble of comprehension was of little value unless it was accompanied by a description of the onset of the malady, its manner of manifestation, plus the conduct and conversation of the individual in daily life. Family history, though vitally important, was not always submitted without evasion, and vague comments about the eccentricities of living and deceased relatives were of little help. A careful and orderly recital of changes in physical health, such as impaired appetite, loss of weight, or lessened vigor, with a full history of any serious illness or grave injury, was of importance. The family physician was asked to note any special disturbance, change in speech, tremor of limbs and facial muscles. All these items assisted the admitting physician in diagnosis. Dr. Brush pointed out to the family that a case of acute mania, even though violent and hard to control, might present a more favorable outlook than a quiet, self-controlled case of paranoia or a complacent paretic. He always urged early admission, for it was the patient placed promptly under care who recovered. In 1907, for example, all the patients discharged as recovered had been brought to the Hospital within six months of the onset of their mental disorder. That year the average length of treatment was four and one-half months, and practically the entire patient population changed during the 12 month period. Brush lamented that the staff saw but a small portion of the psychic picture in each case. Knowledge of the infancy and childhood could be secured only from family and associates whose contact was often casual or irregular.

4. Twenty Years of Service

AT SHEPPARD PRATT, the entire medical staff, including the Physician-in-Chief and his family, lived in the main buildings. After a time it was felt wise to give Dr. Brush some relief from the continuous care of patients by building a house for his family on the grounds. Such a move would also release the suite of rooms he had occupied in the Western Division for additional patients. A New York architect, Mr. E. C. Childs, drew a pleasing design for the new house, which was to be placed on a high point of land some distance from the other buildings. Known as Windy Brae, the house commanded a lovely view of the cultivated fields of the Hospital and the woods beyond. Windy Brae, finished in 1904, was a two-and-one-half story brown-shingled structure with high ceilings, a gracious hall, large drawing rooms, dining room and kitchen on the first floor, and attractive bedrooms above. A barn, large enough for the Superintendent's horse and carriage, was placed at the rear.

With the number of applicants for admission steadily rising, the Trustees decided to build a new structure to house the kitchens and dining rooms, with second-floor space for employees, thus releasing many rooms in the two main buildings for use of patients. At first, this suggested structure was called "A Central Building," but soon, because of its uses, it was known simply as the "Service Building." Work on the new block was to begin as soon as the house for the Superintendent was completed, but construction was delayed by the great Baltimore fire of 1904. This fire, which burned out of control for 30 hours, devoured 500 buildings in the heart of the business area, including many owned and rented by Sheppard Pratt Trustees. Offices of the Trustees, then in the Chamber of Commerce Building on Light Street, were burned, and but for the prompt action of Mr. John C. Davis, the Comptroller, and his clerk,

Alfred W. Strahan, all financial papers of the corporation would have been lost.

Thirteen buildings, mostly warehouses owned by the Trustees, were destroyed. With a book value of $209,000, they were insured for only $103,000. An additional loss of capital and income was suffered from the failure of several fire insurance companies, whose stock the Trustees had inherited from Sheppard. After settlement by insurance companies, the Trustees rebuilt the warehouses. Some of the downtown lots were sold, including one on which a portion of the main building of the Enoch Pratt Free Library was later constructed. The Sheppard Pratt losses were not too great, for Pope, the President, noted that after two years had passed, the income from the endowment yielded as much as it had before the fire. At the end of 1904, the estate held by the corporation was $2,903,731.91

By 1906, the Trustees were ready to consider the low bid of $139,334 given by the John Cowan Construction Company for the new Service Building. This building was in the shape of a T. It was set about 45 feet south of the existing buildings, with a width of 45 feet and a length of 132 feet. A covered corridor, which connected the two main divisions with the Service Building, extended across the front of the new structure forming the base of the "T." The corridor was lined on both sides with large windows that gave pleasing vistas of the grounds. The plan that these corridors might be used as sun rooms or for some type of exercising was never realized.

Four dining rooms, two for men and two for women, were contained in the new building, each supplied with small tables for four people. The kitchens, 40 by 30 feet, had large skylights and side windows; white tile wainscoting assisted sanitation and cleanliness. Diet kitchens, rooms in which to prepare vegetables, and storage spaces completed the first

No. 1

Between 1906 and 1912, the daily program of most patients as follows:

7:00 AM	Clinical observation by hall nurse	1:00 PM-1:30	Dinner
		2:00 PM	Bath
7:00 AM-7:30	Bath	2:30 PM-3:30	Tonic baths
7:30 AM-8:00	Dressing	3:30 PM-4:30	Resting
8:00 AM-8:30	Breakfast	4:30 PM-5:00	Lawn
8:30 AM-10:00	Reading, letter writing	5:00 PM-6:00	Resting, conversation, puzzles, cards, games
10:00 AM-10:45	Calisthenics, volley ball, games	6:00 PM-6:30	Supper
		6:30 PM	Clinical observation
10:45 AM-12:00	Handcrafts	6:45 PM-7:45	On the lawn
12:00 n-1:00 PM	Any diversion, conversation with patients	7:45 PM-8:00	On the ward

No. 2

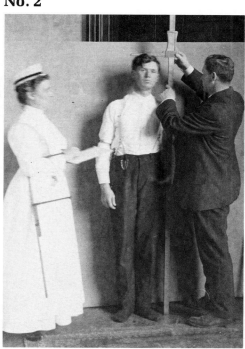

WHAT HAPPENED TO A PATIENT — A DEMONSTRATION SERIES DONE IN 1914
No. 1 TOP: *Arriving at the Hospital, the patient is greeted and assisted from his automobile.*
No. 2 ABOVE: *"Anthropometric" measurements are taken as part of the patient's initial processing.*

The diagnoses of a thousand patients treated at Sheppard Pratt between 1906 and 1912 were as follows:

Diagnosis	1906-7	1907-8	1908-9	1909-10	1910-11	1911-12	Total
Maniacal depression	36	54	26	40	38	38	232
Dementia praecox	38	46	59	51	34	54	282
Paranoia	2	1	2	0	0	1	6
Constitutional psychosis	29	22	33	34	50	23	191
Neurasthenia	15	4	8	3	1	10	41
Climacteric	12	4	9	4	5	1	35
Involutional and senile psychosis	13	9	12	15	6	11	66
Arteriosclerosis	2	4	1	4	2	6	19
Paresis	12	12	7	22	14	18	85
Organic psychosis	3	8	5	3	7	5	31
Toxic psychosis	11	9	7	9	6	12	54
Alcoholic psychosis	10	8	4	4	6	11	43
Traumatic psychosis	0	3	0	0	0	0	3
Not insane	0	2	0	1	1	0	4
Total	183	186	173	190	169	191	1,092

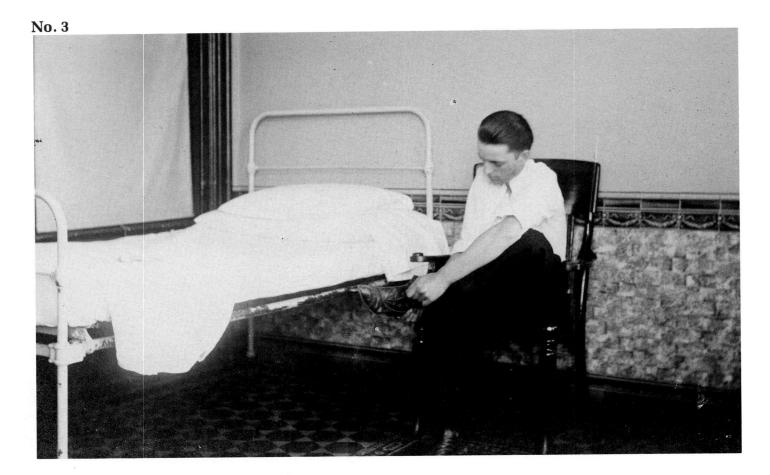

No. 3 ABOVE: *The patient is shown to his room, where he prepares for further examination.*
No. 4 RIGHT: *The patient's case is discussed in a doctor's conference shortly after admission.*
No. 5 BELOW RIGHT: *Later on, the physician conducts complete physical and mental examinations.*

No. 4

No.5

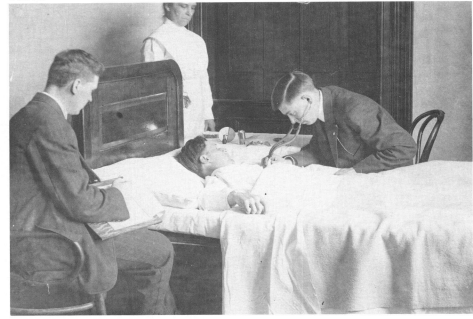

No. 6

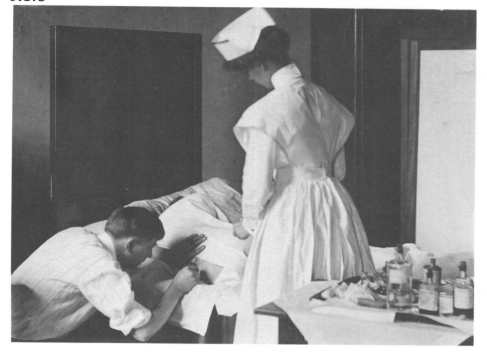

No. 6 LEFT: *As part of the patient's treatment, a lumbar puncture may be administered by the physician.*
No. 7 BELOW: *Hydrotherapy was thought of as the only possible means to quiet a violent patient.*
No. 8 BOTTOM LEFT: *In the meantime, the patient's relatives give his history to the physician.*
No. 9 BOTTOM RIGHT: *A nurse monitors the patient's blood pressure.*

No. 7

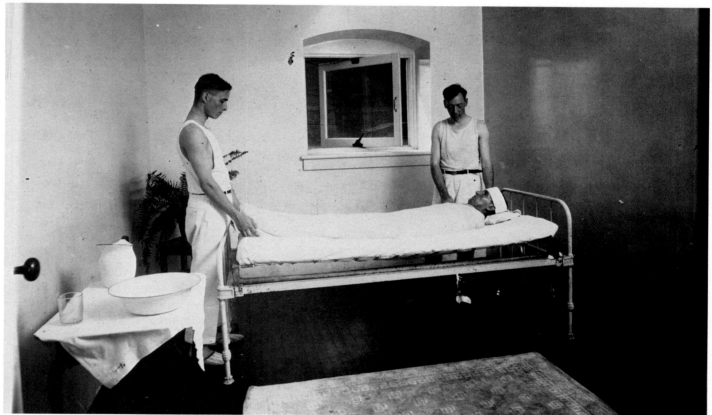

No. 8

No. 9

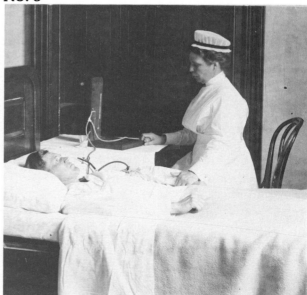

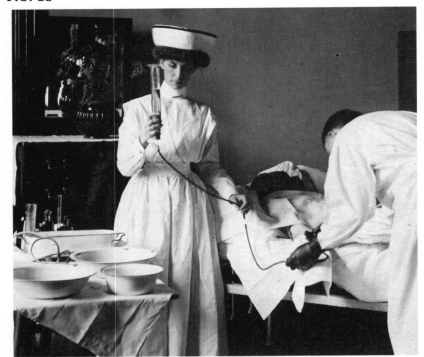

No. 10 RIGHT: *The nurse assists the doctor in administering salvarsan.*
No. 11 BELOW: *Until the introduction of chemotherapy in the late 1920s the wet sheet pack was the only relief available to a patient.*
No. 12 RIGHT: *The patient is seen in the physician's office. Not until the whole staff becomes familiar with his condition and agrees that he is able to return home will he be discharged.*

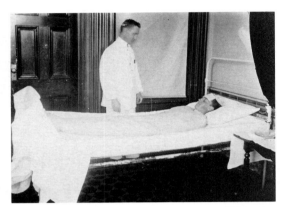

No. 11

floor. Sleeping accommodations for dietary helpers were placed on the second floor on the south side of the Service Building. Bedrooms for nurses, a nurses' parlor, dining room and pantry were on the north side. Cold storage rooms, a meat cutting room, and a dining room for employees filled the basement. The Service Building was ready for use on June 3, 1908. The Trustees borrowed $97,707.70 against their securities to finance the construction.

In 1911, the 20th year of operation at the Hospital, Brush looked over the years just past: "As far as lay in our powers, we have worked together. Trustees, physicians, nurses, and all the numerous employees necessary to the conduct of a hospital, have endeavored to meet the responsibilities thrown upon us. The helpless and dependent have...been aided and cared for with all the resources of the institution. At the same time we have been able to come to the relief of many others. Families and friends have felt the satisfaction which has come from knowing that their sick ones were surrounded by all that experience could suggest in the way of kindness."

The treatment of patients was now stabilized, although there were variations in every case according to the condition of the individual. On admission the patient was given a careful physical examination; those whose physical condition warranted it were given long rest in bed under careful observation. Complete clinical records were made; the individual's mental condition was described by notations such as restlessness, overexcitement, depression, confusion, mutism, resistance to treatment, hallucination and other signs of inward turmoil. In addition, both nurses and physicians jotted down observations on the character and persistence of any delusions or other mark of mental disorder.

Many patients preferred knitting, reading, group games, spending time browsing in the library or weaving in the casino. The male patients spent at least an hour each morning in one of the workshops, and from two to two and a half hours in the afternoon. In the evening, many of the men played pool, card games, or went bowling.

While Brush and his staff felt that some form of occupation, requiring physical and mental effort, was most salutary, they recognized that some patients easily suffered mental fatigue, making it necessary to regulate carefully and direct the time they spent in work or recreation. Other patients with limited attention span could not make the effort necessary to continue at any task longer than a few moments. Gradual reeducation was required by many. Regular classes in handicraft were conducted five days a week by Miss Grace Field. Patients who seemed inaccessible at first often gradually became interested and developed some voluntary initiative. Many individuals began their convalescence by taking up a piece of handwork.

During this period President Theodore Roosevelt was preaching "the strenuous life." However, Brush felt that there was too much preaching and too little attempt to determine who was capable of leading such a life. "The gospel of the age," he remarked, "that of getting on in the world, has left as many mental wrecks in the wake of those who preach it, as were found physical derelicts in the path of the followers of those who preached the crusades. Men and women must be taught their limitations, and taught them before they learn them in the severe school of experience. There are some who can lead the strenuous life, but many there be who must go softly all their days lest disaster overtake them."

With an enlarged medical and nursing staff, improved and more varied diets, growing cost of most articles, and more buildings to service, the expenses of Sheppard Pratt increased steadily. The expenses

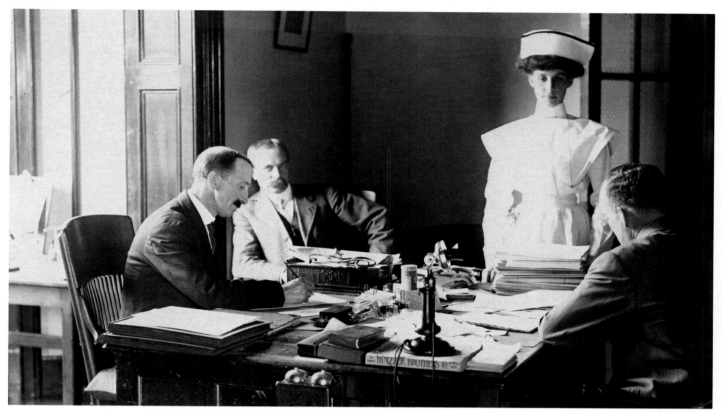

of the Hospital were covered partly by amounts paid by patients and partly by sums taken each year from the endowment income.

Brush reported: "While the Trustees have desired to hold every one to strict accountability for waste or extravagance, they have always maintained a liberal attitude toward any suggestion for improving the standards of care, or the method of treatment. It costs more to cure people than to confine them."

Although Sheppard Pratt had been in operation for only 20 years, the main buildings were now from 30 to 50 years old and beginning to show their age. Two of the main boilers in the power plant had to be replaced. The ice house collapsed. Much of the fire hose was found to be defective, and county inspectors ordered the Trustees to add outside fire escapes to the two main buildings. To increase the supply of ice from the ice pond, a refrigeration plant was purchased. A new athletic field was excavated and graded west of the Casino.

With these pressing repair needs, the Trustees gave much attention to the financial operations of the Hospital and to overseeing the endowment. At the request of the Towson Normal School, they sold two acres of ground for $300 an acre, and the same year purchased 58 acres of land lying between the Hospital and Charles Street as protection against future development. The former home of Enoch Pratt near Mt. Vernon Place, inherited by the Corporation, was sold to Mrs. Mary Washington Keyser for the sum of $55,000. She later gave the building to serve as the home of the Maryland Historical Society, in which both Moses Sheppard and Enoch Pratt had been interested.

In May 1913 the Hospital celebrated the 60th Anniversary of its founding. The event was marked by a bazaar, a field day, an historical address by Brush, and the reading of papers by several other members of the staff. Dr. Adolf Meyer, Director of the newly established Phipps Psychiatric Clinic of The Johns Hopkins Medical School, was present. Brush welcomed the new Hopkins Clinic, saying, "The opening of The Henry Phipps Psychiatric Clinic brings us a welcome ally in the warfare against mental disturbance and mental defect, in the campaign to restore those who have succumbed to the stress and strain of life." He continued, "We shall work hand in hand. Science has no jealousies except those incident to generous rivalry...we shall expect to profit by the investigations carried on by Dr. Meyer."

With these sentiments in mind, arrangements were accordingly made to enable three members of the Sheppard Pratt medical staff to spend part of one day a week in the outpatient department of The Phipps Clinic, and from time to time Meyer lectured at the Hospital. Meyer had a great influence on Sheppard Pratt, as he did on all American psychiatry. As early as 1906, he developed the thesis that dementia praecox was not a disease entity, but a type of reaction that developed in certain personalities as the result of a lack of adaptation, resulting in habit deterioration. His main effort was to secure scientific recognition of the functioning of the human being as the central feature in psychiatry — the psychobiological approach. In his clinic, he insisted on a pluralistic and pragmatic collection of all available facts about a patient as the basis of treatment. He advocated a system of keeping voluminous case records and developing formulations of reaction patterns that gave appropriate consideration to the plasticity, the spontaneity, and the individuality of each patient. It was said of Dr. Meyer that he was one of a small group of psychiatrists largely responsible for the trend that displaced the disciples of the microscope for those of the ward and bedside. His farsighted thinking in time would permeate all of modern psychiatry.

5. New Developments and World War I

THE TRAINING SCHOOL for Nurses proved so valuable that in, 1911, a less extensive course was established for attendants, leading to a certificate. When the 18 month course was successfully completed, attendants were listed in the *Maryland General Directory* as Certified Attendants. At Sheppard Pratt they worked long hours, receiving one-half day a week off duty, and every third Sunday, plus a two-weeks paid vacation. Uniforms were supplied, and attendants were paid $25 a week, plus maintenance and infirmary privileges.

From the beginning, the value of occupational therapy was recognized at Sheppard Pratt. An essential part of the program at the York Retreat in England, it had been copied at the Friends Retreat in Philadelphia. In 1893, a program of light Swedish gymnastics was instituted at Sheppard Pratt, and after the Casino was built the schedule included art work, billiards, bowling, and music. A nine-hole golf course was laid out; tennis was popular; and many baseball games were played between patients, patients and attendants, and with outside teams such as the Towson YMCA, policemen, and firemen. Enthusiasm was so great that the administration provided uniforms for the players. At one period the Sheppard Pratt team was even strengthened by the employment of semi-professionals!

In the winter months, nurses read to groups of patients on the wards — though it was observed that men often fell asleep during the readings; lectures, some illustrated, were arranged; concerts were given; and dramatic productions scheduled. The patients took such pleasure in acting that some of their productions were taken on a "circuit" of other mental institutions such as Springfield and Spring Grove. In a typical winter season, concerts were given at the Hospital by The Johns Hopkins Orchestra, the Glee Club of the State Normal School, the Peabody Institute, the choir boys of St. Paul's School, and the Johns Hopkins University Glee Club. Religious services were held on the first and third Sunday afternoons, conducted by neighborhood clergymen. Brush could say: "There is little in the Hospital that is stagnant or depressing...Every patient who is accessible is given the opportunity to do something."

Outstanding contributions to the development of occupational therapy in the United States were made by Dr. William Rush Dunton, Jr., and Mrs. Henrietta G. Price. Coming to the Hospital in 1895, Dunton remained on the staff for 29 years. He is given credit for the term "occupational therapy," and for committing to paper the basic concept of that activity. These concepts became the foundation of the National Association for the Promotion of Occupational Therapy, of which Dunton was the first President. He was editor of the *Maryland Psychiatric Quarterly* for several years, of the *Journal of Occupational Therapy* from 1923 to 1946, and an associate editor of the *American Journal of Psychiatry* for ten years. He wrote several books, which became standards in his chosen field. Many years later, when the all-year-round swimming pool was constructed at Sheppard Pratt, it was dedicated to Dunton. He recognized that although occupational therapy was no cure-all, it was an important adjunct to other forms of treating the mentally ill.

Mrs. Henrietta G. Price, who followed Dunton as Director of the Occupational Therapy Department, received her training in this field at Johns Hopkins and at St. Elizabeths Hospital in Washington. She was a dynamic individual with great organizing ability, expanding the program until 90% of the patients were included!

In order that nurses might become more companionable with patients, classes were organized for

them by Price. These included the various crafts, nature study, and such group instruction as ''Entertaining the Patient'' and ''Companionship in Nursing.'' Price had eight assistants in the various shops in the Casino, and on the halls — as well as two male aides especially to assist in the more strenuous out-of-door games. Many patients paid for the materials used in craft work and took the finished articles home with them; some made ornaments for their ward; others finished articles that were sold to employees and visitors at the annual bazaar. Much repair of furniture was accomplished by patients in the carpentry shop; and the more skillful made stools, taborets, tables, chairs, and writing desks in which they took much pride. In time, an accredited School of Occupational Therapy was established under Price's leadership; during its first five years of existence 68 students registered for the 16-week course.

Other advances included the 1905 founding of the National Committee for Mental Hygiene following the publication of Clifford W. Beer's book, *The Mind That Found Itself.* An immediate success, this classic autobiography was widely circulated. The author, who had been exposed to brutal and humiliating treatment in several mental institutions, not only exposed evil conditions that existed in some mental hospitals but also advocated practical reforms. He urged the founding of a national organization to wage an educational campaign to inform the public about existing conditions. Next to the need for reform, Beer pointed out the need for prevention in mental illness. Dr. Adolf Meyer, then Director of the New York State Psychiatric Institute, suggested the title ''mental hygiene,'' which became the key term.

With the new emphasis on environmental factors, trained social workers became a necessity in psychiatry. Their training enabled them to take case histories, to deal with families of patients, and to

TOP: *The Board of Trustees of 1912 included Jay Olney Norris, Charles H. Riley, MD, Charles C. Homer, Henry B. Gilpin, Robert K. Waring, W. Champlin Robinson, and Willliam K. Bartlett.*
ABOVE: *Mr. George Oppman shows off a newly-minted reed clothes basket he has just finished.*

follow patients after discharge. Sheppard Pratt was already making use of various social and charitable agencies in the City and Baltimore County — and rendering some services in return. When Dr. William B. Cornell, a former staff member, served as the Executive Secretary of the Maryland Society of Mental Hygiene, he was most cooperative. As early as 1917, Brush asked the Trustees to provide funds in the budget to permit employing a trained social worker to investigate the home surroundings, family, and occupations of applicants for treatment, especially those of limited means.

U.S. entry into the First World War had an immediate effect on Sheppard Pratt. The cost of food and supplies rose rapidly, and help was scarce. Fortunately, Mr. Shipley, who had been in charge of the farm and garden for 30 years, Mr. Shriver, the head carpenter for nearly that length of time, and Mr. Goodwin, the chief engineer, a veteran of 21 years service, all agreed to stay on for the duration. When the country entered the war, the drain on the professional staff was heavy. By 1917 five former assistant physicians were drafted into the armed services, and one was called to serve in a Canadian military hospital. Five Sheppard Pratt nurses were soon on duty in France, and 20 former male nurses went into the army. Soon there were 28 stars on the Hospital service flag. At the Hospital, nurses and patients formed a Red Cross Circle to make garments for refugees and bandages for the wounded.

By 1918, only two assistant physicians were left at Sheppard Pratt, and the shortage of nurses was so great that restrictions had to be placed on admission of turbulent male cases. Dr. L. Gibbons Smart, a former assistant physician who had left the Hospital to become Superintendent of the Maryland School for Feeble Minded Children, returned to be of service. Dr. Noboru Ishide, a Japanese physician sent by his government to study mental treatment in America, joined the staff. The physicians at the Hospital gave as much time as they could spare to local draft boards and to Medical Advisors' Boards. Dr. Stewart Paton, an early director of the Hospital laboratory and an Assistant in Neurology and Psychiatry at The Johns Hopkins Medical School, was one of the early contributors to study in military neuropsychiatric disabilities. He was one of the leaders who recomended establishing psychiatric base hospitals overseas, units near the forward lines for observation and treatment of war neuroses, a psychiatric service for evacuation hospitals, and arrangement for care later in the United States.

Throughout the war Sheppard Pratt was short-handed in every department. Some staff were drafted; others left the Hospital for higher wages given in munitions factories. When harvest time came, painters, carpenters, plumbers, laundry workers, and warehouse clerks helped in the fields; hours were extended; vacations were canceled. To reduce the need for farm workers, the Trustees purchased a hayloader and tractor.

Despite the need to tighten the belt, Brush could report that ''Nothing that was necessary to care and treatment of the patients was permitted to fall behind, but some items had to be postponed of necessity. Some things could not be had, or were only obtained after long delay.''

Owing to the great shortage of workers in the dietary department, a cafeteria service was introduced for nurses and other employees. This system proved so valuable and popular that the housekeeper declared she hoped never to give it up because it saved so much food! A modern dishwashing machine was also installed.

In spite of the shortage of help, the farm and garden provided ready supplies of food for the Hospital.

BELOW: *Nurses Fulton and Dorsey relaxing over a game of cribbage in 1919.*
RIGHT: *The Nursing class of 1916. Miss Matheson, Mrs. Headly, Miss Mary Gillis, and Miss Mary Eve Harrell.*

Milk, fresh vegetables, and fruit were produced. The garden was extended and vegetables that were not immediately consumed by the patients were canned for future use. Several acres of sweet corn were planted, and several hundred bushels of potatoes were raised. The older milk cows were slaughtered for beef and the young male calves for veal. Refuse from the kitchens had always been fed to pigs on the grounds; during wartime, supplementary grains were purchased to increase the supply of pork. The first of two silos was constructed to store ensilage and so increase the production of milk.

A side effect of the war was the discontinuation of the pathological laboratory, and its space was turned into bedrooms. Although the war hastened its demise, this line of research had not produced sufficient knowledge to warrant its continuation.

At this time, the local courts began to send some cases to the Hospital for diagnosis, the judges making it clear that the mental evaluation of the accused would influence the decision for disposition of the case. Two drug cases were admitted, but again Dr. Brush indicated to the Trustees that he did not think Sheppard Pratt could serve such individuals.

During the war there were four distressing suicides, one or more of which might be attributed to the shortage of attendants and nurses. A woman "eloped," eluded the nurse searching for her, and drowned herself in a nearby pond. A male patient ran away from his escort and returned to his home. The Hospital asked for his return, fearing that he would harm himself, but the family refused. Shortly afterwards, he committed suicide. A third patient borrowed money from a friend, fled to another state, purchased a gun, and shot himself. After another woman surreptitiously took money from a visitor, she broke parole by going to a nearby drugstore where she purchased a bottle of bichloride of mer-

cury tablets, which she took with fatal results. And wartime pressures did not only produce unfortunate results with the patients; the staff was also greatly shocked when the Japanese doctor, Noboru Ishide, shot and killed Dr. George B. Wolf, an assistant physician. Ishide was found to be mentally disordered himself, believing that Wolf considered him to be a spy in the employ of his government!

Group confrontation was not exclusive to the European front. In 1917 the Trustees won a very important legal battle which had wide ramifications and was of great importance to all eleemosynary institutions. A city fireman broke an arm while fighting a blaze in a downtown warehouse owned by Sheppard Pratt. He sued the Hospital for $10,000, claiming negligence on the part of the owners because of a defective fire escape which, he claimed, caused his injury. The case went to the Maryland Court of Appeals, where it was won by the Sheppard Pratt Trustees. The court ruled that a trust fund, established for a charitable purpose, could not be destroyed by a negligent act of those employed to administer the charity. The decision was to stand in Maryland for nearly 50 years.

The war affected finances for the Trustees, as increasing costs forced the Board to allocate a larger portion of their yearly income to the operation of the Hospital. But, oddly enough, between 1913 and 1920 there were fewer requests for free care, and the number who paid only a portion of the cost of their treatment did not fluctuate greatly.

The Trustees were not idle during the war years. W. Champlin Robinson was named by the President of the United States as Director of Fuel Conservation for the country; Charles C. Homer was Chairman of the Executive Committee for the Fourth Liberty Loan in Maryland. Two important Trustees died during this period, George A. Pope, and Dr. Charles H. Riley.

6. A Change in Leadership

DURING HIS TWENTY-FIVE years as Physician-in-Chief and Superintendent, Dr. Brush was elected President of the Medico-Psychological Association, a predecessor of the American Psychiatric Association. This was a fitting recognition, for Brush had planned the work of the Hospital in keeping with the desires of the Founder, established its clinical procedures, laid down a sound financial and administrative policy, and advanced its reputation in the medical profession. He attracted to Sheppard Pratt a group of young physicians whom he led in sound medical practices and whom he stimulated to effective labors in clinical and pathological research.

In his presidential address before the Medico-Psychological Association in New Orleans, April 4, 1916, Brush lamented that many of the medical profession took little interest in psychiatry, and either ignored or held warped and distorted views concerning its efforts. Brush thought that assistant physicians should be appointed on probation and should receive permanent tenure only after passing examinations in psychiatry. In this he foresaw the time when a national testing program would be established for the certification of psychiatrists. He proposed that laboratories be better equipped, and urged closer cooperation between general and psychiatric clinics. He believed that outpatient clinics should make prompt care more possible and that staffs of mental hospitals should be interested in community health as well as in their own patients. Brush urged that a pension system be created for employees of mental hospitals and that staff positions be removed from politics. He mentioned one state institution that had had nine superintendents in 13 years, none of whom had previous training in psychiatry!

On September 1, 1919, Brush, then 67 years of age, presented his resignation as Physician-in-Chief and Medical Superintendent to the Trustees. Brush was appointed Medical Superintendent Emeritus, and continued to direct the Hospital until a successor was found. Brush remained as Editor of the *American Journal of Psychiatry* for another 12 years.

On April 1, 1920, Dr. Ross McC. Chapman took over as Medical Superintendent and Physician-in-Chief as an exponent of psychoanalytical practice. Chapman was an Instructor in Psychiatry at George Washington University and later served as an assistant and then Professor of Psychiatry at the University of Maryland. During the First World War, he was commissioned a Major and Divisional Psychiatrist of the Sixth Division in the Army of Occupation in Germany. During the Second World War, he was a member of the Medical Examiners at the Armed Forces Induction Station in Baltimore, receiving the Selective Service Medal for his work.

After studying the interpretive notes left by Moses Sheppard, Chapman reported to the Board of Trustees that he saw the work of the Hospital falling into three parts. First was the study of the patients, their care and treatment. In certain cases, treatment consisted of affording protection from the stresses previously existing in the patient's environment; a breathing space for rest; self-study; and a careful review of resources, mental and physical, before a fresh start was undertaken. In some cases, analytical treatment was indicated; in others, the emphases would be on arousing new interests. The second duty of the Hospital was to forward psychiatric research by encouraging members of the staff to undertake the study of special psychiatric problems. The third duty lay in education.

At the end of his first year as Medical Superintendent, Chapman reported to the Trustees: "There can be no change of administration without an accompanying unrest and disquiet on the part of many em-

Fabian Bachrach

ABOVE: *Dr. Ross McClure Chapman, second Medical Director, took over his duties as Medical Superintendant and Physician-in-Chief on April 1, 1920. He remained in office until 1948.*

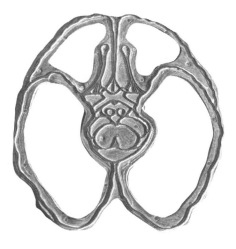

ployees, which it takes a little while to overcome…but this unrest seems to be abating (for) the Hospital organization was fundamentally sound.'' He found ''deplorable inertia and a most unpleasant number of bad habits existing in the working methods of most departments.'' Many of these came about due to the pressure of wartime conditions and the unavoidable shortages of help. Ward attendants were discontented with long hours, and with their wages, which were (with maintenance) $40 a month the first year and $50 a month the second year. Chapman told the Trustees that there were pressing needs for such items as an assembly hall, stage, gymnasium, and occupational therapy quarters.

The first innovation made by Chapman was the appointment of a staff of consultants who gave time to special needs at Sheppard Pratt. Among those willing to serve in this capacity were some of the best known specialists in the city, such as Dr. Walter A. Baetjer, Dr. Sydney R. Miller, Dr. Walter E. Dandy, Dr. Thomas S. Cullen, Dr. Hiram Wood, Dr. William S. Baer, and Dr. Herbert F. Gorgas. Fees of the consultants were added to the patient's bill or were covered by the Hospital.

Chapman gave considerable attention to the library, working closely with Miss Helen Carleton and her successor, Miss Helen M. Richards. The library was open in the morning six days a week and during two afternoons. Monday evenings it was used by nurses and attendants. The librarian made two visits a week to each ward, and books and magazines were taken about in a remodeled tea cart. There was a wide selection of books in the patients' library, the total reaching two thousand. Circulation of books in the library had a hearty increase, and by 1930, the number of volumes in the patients' library was 5,416.

The medical library of over one thousand books was under the care of the patients' librarian with the

LEFT: *A zinc plate of the brain stem, used in the printing of texts for the nursing staff in the '20s.*
RIGHT: *A copper and galvanized still, whose use was (hopefully) confined to laboratory experiments during Prohibition.*
BELOW: *An aerial view of the Hospital taken in 1929.*

help of a number of physicians, who gave considerable time to enhancing its usefulness. Sixty-two medical and psychiatric journals were received by subscription. Thirty-two psychiatrists, many former assistants at Sheppard Pratt, sent their reprints to the Hospital.

Chapman set up a schedule of five staff meetings at noon, at which admissions and recommendations for discharges were considered. Steps were taken to enlarge the staff, and by 1923 there were nine physicians employed, with one intern, Grace Baker, MD. Physicians received from $1,500 to $4,000 a year with maintenance. General nurses were paid from $1,800 and $2,000 a year with maintenance.

In December of 1922 Chapman brought to Sheppard Pratt Dr. Harry Stack Sullivan, one of the two most influential psychiatrists ever associated with the Hospital. Sullivan (1892-1949) was the son of a poor Irish farmer in upstate New York. He received his education at the Chicago College of Medicine and various public hospitals. At St. Elizabeths Hospital in Washington, DC, he came under the influence and encouragement of Dr. William A. White. Superintendent White was one of the earliest and most prominent physicians to adopt the Freudian orientation toward psychiatric problems. He was keenly interested in the genetic conception of psychiatry as well as the relation of his profession to sociology. White regarded mental disease as an abnormal reaction of the individual to his human needs in relation to his social setting. He assisted in founding the *Psychoanalytical Review*, which gave his ideas wide circulation. With the background received at St. Elizabeths, Sullivan applied Freud's thinking in an effort to understand and treat the individual. In time, through his activities as a clinical psychiatrist, Sullivan disagreed with some Freudian concepts. He became the exponent of "the so-called dynamic-cultural school of psychoanalysis, which emphasized sociological rather than biological events, present day contacts with people rather than infantile sexuality." He ceased to be an orthodox Freudian.

In the seven years that Sullivan was at Sheppard Pratt, he remained primarily interested in schizophrenic patients. Out of his clinical research came such of his early papers as: "Schizophrenia: Its Conservation and Malignant Features"; "Peculiarity of Thought in Schizophrenia"; "Affective Experience in Early Schizophrenia"; "The Onset of Schizophrenia"; and "Research in Schizophrenia." After Sullivan left the Hospital, he wrote many papers based on his work at the Hospital and outlined more fully his concept of psychiatry as the science of interpersonal relations.

Sullivan was given a free hand with his work while at Sheppard Pratt; he had a ward of his own, where he worked without interference from others. His patients were young male schizophrenics; he allowed no female nurses on his section. Said a nurse from that period: "Sullivan was a rather awesome person, but with a twinkle in his piercing brown eyes. He was courteous and seemed appreciative when small personal requests were met. He was not always in accord with the decisions of the nursing service administration, nor was he always in agreement with the nursing care policies for his patients."

In 1921 Chapman brought to Sheppard Pratt its first trained social worker, Susan H. Kubie. She was followed by Mary B. Glackin. In her second year Glackin made 485 visits inside the Hospital and 367 visits to former patients and families outside Sheppard Pratt. She took the case histories of patients, maintained contact with paroled or discharged patients, helped in the transfer of individuals to other institutions, assisted with physical examinations,

and made contact with the University of Maryland dispensary. Chapman felt that activities of social workers were so valuable that he gave an extended outline to the Trustees of their usefulness. "It is an accepted fact," said Dr. Chapman, "that the responsibilites of a psychiatric hospital towards its patients do not cease upon the discharge of the patient." He commented on the fact that the patient who was unable to adjust to his environment was often thrust back into the same situation on release from the hospital. A totally different environment was often necessary if the patient's improvement was to continue. Here the task of the social worker was to give the family an understanding of the individual's problem and some idea how they could help him. She could assist the family in securing a new environment in which the patient could consolidate his improvement, and she could also help the patient establish and retain his self-confidence.

In the 1920's admissions to Sheppard Pratt varied from 210 to 274, discharges were from 191 to 279 a year. Of those discharged, 39% were manic depressive, 23 listed as dementia praecox. The Superintendent reported that only cases offering hope of recovery were admitted; alcoholics and drug addicts were not knowingly taken for treatment.

In the area of physical improvements, Chapman carried through a number of useful changes. The furnaces in the power plant were converted from coal to oil; two artesian wells were sunk, each to the depth of 200 feet; a five-car metal garage was constructed, and much work was accomplished on the roads; all this amounting to approximately $40,000. Baltimore County purchased 4.7 acres of land on a portion of the Sheppard Pratt property for a sewage disposal plant, paying $500 an acre for the land.

A novel accommodation was made for a wealthy gentleman from the South who desired his daughter to live in her own home under the care of the Sheppard Pratt staff; arrangements were made to carry out his wishes. Fordham, or the Poe Cottage, built on a beautiful knoll at a cost of more than $20,000, was occupied by Miss Poe for nearly 40 years, after which the house reverted to the Trustees.

Chapman believed it would be greatly to the advantage of the staff physicians if houses could be constructed on the grounds for them; because of lack of houses, married physicians did not wish to remain long at the Hospital. Preliminary plans, which were drawn several times, were always discarded because of the costs involved. In 1926, however, the Trustees decided to build a larger house on the grounds for the Medical Superintendent. This was done, and in December of 1927, Dr. and Mrs. Chapman moved into "Overlook." This was a charming, spacious, two and a-half story brick house, with a tiled eastern porch from which the occupants could see across the eastern valley toward Towson Normal School. The cost exceeded $50,000. "Overlook" became a delightful center of social life for the physicians, especially through the weekly afternoon teas presided over by Mrs. Chapman.

The farm and garden continued to be very productive, with Miss Alma E. Bering, for many years a most efficient dietician and manager, canning between six and eight thousand quarts of fruits and vegetables each year. There were misfortunes, however. Twenty pigs were lost through cholera in 1924, and in the same year the cow barn was destroyed by fire. The money loss in stock and building amounted to nearly $45,000, an amount only partially covered by insurance. When the cow barn was rebuilt, it was considerably enlarged, and at the same time, the piggery was supplied with running water and electricity. Garbage from the kitchens was boiled in huge vats before being fed to the pigs.

7. Expansion

DR. CHAPMAN MAINTAINED that an efficient and industrious staff, given proper equipment and a productive research department, would continue to attract the attention of medical and scientific leaders, keep the beds occupied as they were at present, and warrant enlarged facilities. He hoped to increase the usefulness of the upper floors of the main buildings; to secure more adequate quarters for physicians and nurses; and to create an arrangement for the better classification of patients. When the Rockefeller Foundation expressed an interest in Sheppard Pratt, it was hoped that a contribution would be made toward a building program. The Director of the Foundation wrote to Chapman: "You have it in your power to develop a very remarkable institution here. It has been properly regarded from the beginning as an outstanding hospital for the care of the mentally sick people, but it should and may easily occupy a much greater position of prominence in the medical and scientific world."

Propitious words, these, but unfortunately there was to be no contribution from this or any other foundation for another 40 years!

In 1926 William G. Nolting, a Baltimore architect, was asked to design a building for 80 beds, with the specific needs of newly admitted patients in mind. These patients were to be admitted in reassuring surroundings, out of sight of visitors and officers, and away from disorderly patients. Provisions were made so that deranged individuals could be moved from one area to another without passing through long corridors. In order to maintain a quiet atmosphere for patients, utility rooms, kitchens, bathrooms, and the recreation area were to be placed at some distance from the wards. Nolting presented to the Board plans for a building of colonial design, which was to be located on a natural plateau about 1,000 feet away from the older structures. Facing northeast, the building would afford an extensive view of the Green Spring Valley. The Trustees approved Nolting's design, and the building — in the shape of the letter E, three stories high, and 264 feet long — was constructed. Plans included a hydrotherapy department to occupy a one-story addition, 75 feet long, on the western end.

Reflecting careful planning by the Medical Staff and Trustees, the new building allowed newly admitted patients to enter an attractive reception room containing a cheerful fireplace on the east end of the ground floor. Located down the hall were admission and examination offices, conference rooms, and doctors' offices. Rooms for visiting specialists — such as the orthopedist, gynecologist, neurologist, optometrist, dentist and urologist — were close by, as were rooms for X-ray apparatus and its technicians. Laboratories were also located on the ground floor. Necessary service rooms, nurses' stations, sun rooms, and occupational therapy rooms were placed conveniently close to the various wards.

It was expected that the Reception Building with its furnishings would cost in the neighborhood of $350,000, but as usual the estimate fell far short of the reality. When final bills were paid by the Trustees, the cost totaled $715,431.47.

To cover the cost of the Reception Building, the Trustees borrowed $400,000 from the Baltimore Savings Bank, slowly liquidating the debt from the Trustees' income and Hospital operating surplus. In planning and constructing the Reception Building, the Trustees followed the direction of Enoch Pratt's earlier request that the Hospital, if possible, should be enlarged by 200 beds.

The dedication of the Reception Building was held on May 18, 1929. On that date, however, painting of many rooms and laying of the terrazzo and mastic floors had not been completed. Equipment and furni-

RIGHT: *A Studebaker from an earlier era, belonging to W.L. Patterson. Mr. Westermeyer is behind the wheel and George Opman is the passenger.*

BELOW: *Dedicated in 1929, the Reception Building was designed with the needs of newly admitted patients in mind. Provisions were made so that deranged individuals could be moved from one area to another without passing through long corridors. Now called the Chapman Building, this is how the structure looks today.*

BOTTOM: *A fine photo of B Building, taken around 1913.*

ABOVE: Dr. William Ross Dunton doing a bit of woodworking in the occupational therapy shop. Dunton is generally credited with coining the term "occupational therapy." **TOP:** Sheppard Pratt's nursing staff; a group photo probably taken around 1919. **OPPOSITE TOP:** The Hospital's baseball team of 1919. Baseball was so popular with patients and staff that the administration seeded the roster with semi-professionals!

ture were on hand in storage. On that occasion the Medical Superintendent Emeritus, Dr. Edward N. Brush, spoke on "History and Retrospection," followed by Dr. Chapman's address on "Problems of the Modern Psychiatric Hospital." Sullivan spoke on research and treatment of schizophrenia, while Dr. William A. White, Superintendent of St. Elizabeths Hospital in Washington, also gave a major address.

With the new reception building, the Hospital admission routine now became standardized. Within 24 hours of entering Sheppard Pratt the patient was given a complete physical examination, followed within ten days by a mental examination. Reports from the attending physician, the oculist, dentist, and other specialists soon were placed in the patient's file. As complete a personal history of the patient as securable was taken, including his early environment, family, childhood, and adolescent days. The story of his maturity included domestic life, personal attributes, business activities; and any traumatic events experienced. This searching investigation, the staff believed, uncovered a considerable part of the difficulties of the patient, and was helpful in his rehabilitation.

In 1924, Dr. Arthur Ellis Pattrell became the First Assistant Physician and Assistant Superintendent. A splendid administrator and a stern, methodical and efficient doctor, he was respected by all. He made the initial contact with the families, arranged the rates, and remained close to each patient, making rounds and visiting the patients everyday. He was a mainstay of the active work at Sheppard Pratt until his death in 1945. Dr. Lewis B. Hill served as Clinical Director from 1928 to 1930. After resigning, he was absent for a period but returned to give dedicated service at a later date. Sullivan carried on his clinical research with the assistance of two

psychologists, three clinical assistants, and a stenographer. Dunton was physician in charge of occupational therapy. Dr. G. Wilson Shaffer joined the staff as chief psychologist, organized and developed that department, and continued his useful work for 40 years at Sheppard Pratt. During this time he also served as Chairman of the Department of Psychology at Johns Hopkins University and later Dean of the University.

The pathology laboratory was reorganized and refitted by Dr. Joseph M. Looney, who was a trained research chemist from Harvard University. In a single year, Looney made 526 laboratory tests, including 238 blood counts, 108 diabetic urine tests, 231 Wasserman tests, and 38 tests of spinal fluid. He analyzed many samples, seeking to find a relationship between nitrogenous constituent variations and types of mental disease. His findings corroborated the fact that there existed in the blood of markedly depressed patients a toxic substance. He believed that he had discovered the existence of an increased amount of creatine in the blood of catatonic patients and a decreased amount of calcium. Reports of his findings were published in several medical journals. After he left Sheppard Pratt, this special research was discontinued for lack of a suitably trained laboratory worker to carry on.

Along with his myriad of medical and administrative responsiblities, Chapman held a keen personal interest in the manic-depressive psychoses. He felt they could all be regarded as based on difficulties of adaption, and reactions to conditions of stress, conscious or unconscious. He felt they represented a constructive effort, the patient's way of handling a difficult or impossible situation, or a conflict into the nature of which the patient might have little or no insight. To treat such patients, careful individual study was necessary, as well as action

on the part of the physician based on knowledge of the peculiar problems that evolved from this study. In the manic-depressive group, Chapman observed manifestations such as excitement, depression, stupors, mixed states, and transitional states. A good prognosis resulted if the patient maintained good contact with reality and the extroverted type of thought and action characteristic of the normal person. No special etiology was characteristic of this group; he felt heredity played some part, but was not sure what part to ascribe to it in a given case. More important than transmission of germ plasm, he declared, were the multitudinous and incessant environmental stimuli that consciously mold the personality, particularly during the early developmental years. There usually was a precipitating factor, a more or less difficult situation, to which the individual appeared unable to adjust; this might be the loss of a near relative or friend, marriage, sexual assault, or other traumatic experience, or continuous emotional pressure of a specific kind. Harder to evaluate were the deeper, unconscious strivings and cravings which could not be gratified or tolerated in consciousness and which came to be expressed in the psychotic symptoms.

Many of these patients, Chapman noted, previous to the breakdown, were timid, submissive, and shrinking, often dominated by a relative. As the individual struggled for peace and security, he was faced with the danger of being overwhelmed by the appearance in full consciousness of unconscious cravings. In the manic, his hyperactivity served to protect him from consciousness of his special conflict. He was running away. During talks between the therapist and patient, often the source of the conflict was disclosed, which frequently was found to be somewhat erotic or religious.

After the construction of the reception building

LEFT: *Farmer Frank Shipley working the Hospital's tractor on a corn harvest, circa 1915. It must have been a hot day, because the men have removed the engine cover.*
RIGHT: *A scene from the main kitchen during the preparation of luncheon trays during the World War I era.*

the number of patients received and discharged rose rapidly. In a 1927 report, Chapman explained that the staff was conservative in its estimate of recoveries. A patient was not discharged as cured unless the staff was confident the individual could return home and take up his normal activities, although at some time in the future a second break might occur. Those who were discharged "much improved" might seem normal, but there was a question whether under the pressures of their environment they would remain stable. Failing to make a satisfactory adjustment at home, some patients continued in a semi-invalid state or returned to the Hospital. Of those discharged in 1927, 62 were regarded as being considerably or permanently of value to their family and society.

With the building of the Reception Building, increased staff accommodations were needed. Unused spaces on the third floor of both A and B Buildings (once called Eastern and Western Divisions) were equipped with plumbing and these provided many rooms for attendants and office personnel.

Because additional rooms were also necessary for nurses, two wings were added to the former residence of the Medical Superintendent. Nolting drew very practical and pleasing plans for brick additions to Windy Brae. Contract for the new construction was let in 1929 and the building was ready for occupancy in 1931. The total cost, with furnishings, was nearly $400,000. Each student nurse's room, which had running water, was furnished with bed, study table, desk, and chair. The enlargement of Windy Brae also released rooms for 25 patients in the older buildings, raising the total capacity of the Hospital to 280.

In place of the older Training School, a new program of instruction for nurses was now established. A recent Maryland law required all graduate nurses to be trained in psychiatric nursing, and Sheppard Pratt was the only hospital in the state equipped to teach a large number of students in psychiatry at one time. Affiliations were arranged with a number of general hospitals to send their undergraduate students to Sheppard Pratt for three months of training; graduate students who had not received the required amount of psychiatric training were also admitted to the same course.

Graduate nurses who came for their special psychiatric training at Sheppard Pratt made a valuable contribution on the various halls. In addition to their other classes, they were assigned to the Occupational Therapy Department and received 20 lectures on social case work. Each week, they spent one day with the Children's Aid Society in Towson and another day in the Juvenile Court. They visited other correctional institutions, and in the summer observed camps maintained for underprivileged or handicapped children. Their experience was much enriched by the period spent at Sheppard Pratt.

In 1927 there were just over 100 persons in the Nursing Department, under the skilled direction of Miss Mary S. Moylan. The department included supervising and charge nurses, postgraduate and student nurses, 28 women attendants and 31 male attendants, the sewing woman and a linen room caretaker. After the Reception Building was in service, the number nearly doubled.

The standard weekly rate for patients during the late 1920's was $45. If a family applied for admission of a member at much below the normal rate, and there was considerable uncertainty whether or not treatment at Sheppard Pratt would be effective, the family was informed that the Hospital might not be able to retain the individual. In such a case, it was the duty of the social worker to see that the name of the individual was entered on the free list in the office of the Supervisor of City Charities.

During this expansion period of the 1920s, it became necessary to reorganize the Housekeeping Department. Up until this time, the department was directed by the Superintendent of Nurses. Now a woman was engaged to oversee the porters and maids and supervise the general housekeeping. She had charge of all cleaning, care of rugs, draperies, mattresses, linens, laundry, and mending, as well as the marking room. In the latter, about a thousand garments belonging to patients were marked and listed each month; and, on the average, four hundred articles mended. In choosing the Housekeeper, Chapman commented: "I want a woman who is tactful, of a pleasing personality, able to meet many and varied types of personalities, with proper social instincts, and a gentlewoman." Miss Ruth Parker, a college graduate with special training, fulfilled all the desired criteria and was a great strength.

Changes were also necessary in the business office. Marvin Merryman was appointed in June of 1929 to take the place of John C. Davis, the efficient and conscientious purveyor who resigned after a long tenure of service. In addition to Merryman, a part-time bookkeeper and clerical worker was needed. Chapman told the Trustees that, because of the increased paper work, he needed a girl who "would take care of all office work, and making out bills. This would relieve the music director who now takes care of this work, and make it possible for her to devote full time to music, a phase of treatment that has proven invaluable!" Stenographers received $75 a month with maintenance, and typists $60. Laundry workers — usually a hospital's most poorly paid workers — received $1.75 a day with maintenance.

Whenever it came time for several long-term employees to retire, the Trustees discussed establishing a pension system but always decided it would be too expensive a move. When Albert Stifler retired after 37 years of employment, and George Goodwin, chief engineer, after 38 years, each was given one-half his usual pay. Allen Brown, who had been assistant engineer for several decades, took Goodwin's position and remained in charge of the power plant for another 25 years.

A special budget committee of the Trustees worked with the Medical Superintendent in establishing a monthly budget for all operating expenses, but in spite of every care taken, it continued to rise from the mid 1920s through the mid 1930s.

For many years a special celebration was held on Founder's Day, May 16; and a wreath was placed on the grave of Moses Sheppard in Greenmount Cemetery at Christmas and Easter time, although it is doubtful if the Founder would have approved such an expenditure.

When Overlook was constructed, the antique furniture from Moses Sheppard's house was placed in the home of the Medical Superintendent, and the Trustees directed that it should never be scattered over the buildings. His library remained in the reception room of the A Building. When the central building of the Enoch Pratt Free Library was completed, the Trustees presented to the library a collection of newspapers accumulated by the Founder between 1790 and 1857. Some of the newspapers had been indexed by Moses Sheppard himself, one set ranging from 1799 to 1856.

The sixth President of the Board of Trustees, W. Champlin Robinson, died on October 31, 1930. He had been elected a Board member in 1908 and became President in 1919. William K. Bartlett, like Robinson a member of the Society of Friends, became a Trustee in 1912, and Vice-President in 1919. As Chairman of the Farm and Property Committee, he gave uncounted hours to their improvement. He died on January 12, 1930.

8. Effects of the Great Depression

ALTHOUGH DR. CHAPMAN was instrumental in motivating the Trustees to increase the physical facilities of Sheppard Pratt, perhaps his major contribution was in improving the treatment program. The prevailing ideals of moral or humane treatment, which called for pleasing and comfortable surroundings, sympathetic attention, opportunities for recreation, occupational therapy, employment, and hydrotherapy were well established before Chapman came to Sheppard Pratt; his greatest contribution would be the introduction of individual psychotherapy.

Chapman pointed out, "These efforts might pass through all the stages of ineffectiveness, incompetency, social, emotional, and intellectual maladaptation, to profound mental disorder. Thus many reach adult years with badly warped personalities." The Medical Superintendent went on: "The roots of failure and mental illness are usually to be found buried in childhood and adolescence...Problem children include the overshy, oversensitive, seclusive, moody, the incorrigible, the truant, those subject to temper tantrums, the spoiled child, the dreamer and others. Investigation almost always discovers the reason therefore in the immediate environment, that is, the home life of the child or in his relationships outside the home with his playmates." It was unfortunately true.

Dr. Chapman became acquainted with the works of Freud while at the Binghamton State Hospital; later he took a course under August Hoch, one of the early exponents of Freud's methods in America. While serving as first assistant physician at St. Elizabeths, he worked with William Alanson White, one of the most influential proponents of psychoanalysis in the United States. It was said of White that he contributed more than any other American psychiatrist to a recognition of the dynamic factors in the causation of mental illness. Chapman, along with Meyer, White, and Hoch, was one of the founders of the American Psychoanalytic Association and a founder of the Washington-Baltimore Psychoanalytic Society.

Chapman believed that psychoanalysis was a useful method of treatment in certain cases, and was stimulating and provocative of thought and effort in many others. In the mental hospital, there were a limited number who could be treated by this method, for the case load of the hospital physician made it impossible for him to give the required time; but the insights gained from the psychoanalytic approach could be adapted to psychotherapy. At this time the case load of most physicians at The Sheppard Pratt Hospital was 30, and Chapman thought this should be reduced to ten if the psychoanalytic method was practiced. He felt it was of immense value, however, to have physicians trained in analysis who could apply psychoanalytic theory to many of the psychotic patients, and who could inject into staff discussions the psychoanalytic viewpoint.

Chapman held that there was no exclusive theory concerning the nature of mental illness, nor any specific and exclusive form of treatment applicable to all cases. He noted that the well-ordered daily regimen scheduled for the patient and residence in the hospital away from the irritations and burdens of life were in themselves sufficient methods of treatment for a considerable number of patients. The fact that the patient recognized that the doctor was interested in him as an individual was also of inestimable value.

He spoke of the rapid increase in the number of psychiatrists in private practice, in education, and industry. He emphasized that "the heart of psychiatry must be hospital psychiatry. It is in the hospital," he declared, "that psychiatrists are

TOP: *The Superintendent's office in 1920. Notice the spike "filing system" to the right of the window.*
ABOVE: *In order that the garden, farm and dairy might make a full contribution to the upkeep of the Hospital, Mr. J. Frank Shipley was put in charge of all outdoor operations.*

LEFT: *The hospital's cattle prospered until 1931, when malta fever attacked the herd.*
BELOW: *Folk dancing was an enjoyable pastime.*
RIGHT: *A portion of the north lawn used as a putting green.*

developed. The Hospital must continue as a post-graduate center."

On October 29, 1929, the end of the postwar prosperity came with the stock market crash; millions were lost by speculators and others. In spite of the financial crisis, Chapman told the Trustees in 1930 that the per capita income from patients could be maintained provided the quality of medical and nursing care was maintained. The next year he wrote in his annual report, "In this year of widespread financial and psychological depression, of widespread unemployment and marked decrease in income on the part of the well-to-do, we have before us the task nevertheless of conducting the operations of the Hospital with the same objectives as during the year just ended; namely, the Hospital must support itself, pay for its own operations. It must accomplish this without changing the character of its service rendered or modifying to any material extent its benevolences. This, gentlemen, is apt to be difficult but I have no fears regarding the outcome." A little later that year, he encouraged them by saying, "This Hospital, we can with all modesty say, is an outstanding institution of its kind, engaged in a special technical work of first importance. There are very few hospitals like it doing the sort of work it does in this country...In this field of medicine, we are still in our pioneer days."

In the first five years of the Depression, the income from patients did not cover the operating expenses of the Hospital. Every effort was made to reduce expenditures, without, however, reducing the quality of care or the quality of food served. William Brewster, Jr., Chairman of the Executive Committee, and the President of the Board, met with the Superintendent each week to scrutinize all expenditures. In June of 1932, salaries for the month were reduced 25%, and then changed to a standard reduc-

tion for all of 5%. Department budgets were cut, and vacancies never filled. The allowance for student nurses was cut from $25 a month to $10, then to $5. Lewis Johnson, who had worked for Sheppard Pratt for 35 years, was retired on a pension of $15 a month, with the comment, "there is always the chance of the Lord calling him hence." It was decided to give no further pensions until times improved.

The per capita cost of patients between 1925 and 1929 had averaged $53.11 a week, and the per capita income was $47.79, leaving a deficit of $5.32 per patient, which had to be covered from endowment funds. With careful economies, Chapman cut the patient cost, and kept expenses remarkably close to the income.

At the start of the Depression, the most severe loss to the Hospital was that of Dr. Harry Stack Sullivan, who resigned in the spring of 1930. Sullivan's major contribution was in clinical psychiatry, and his emphasis on interpersonal relationships opened the way to applying dynamic psychotherapeutic techniques to schizophrenia. He emphasized sociological rather than biological events, everyday contacts with people rather than past events, and current interpersonal relationships rather than infantile sexuality.

Sullivan assisted in the design of a small six-bed ward in the Reception Building, complete with sitting rooms and bath, shut off from the rest of the floor. This area was for young male schizophrenics, because Sullivan once said that he could not study female schizophrenics without getting more puzzled than they were! In this ward, all the personnel were male, and each nurse and attendant was picked for his capacity to give of himself to the patients under his care. Sullivan thought of the schizophrenic illness as primarily an unsuccessful reaction to severe anxiety, as ways of interacting with other individuals were not very different from the interpersonal pro-

cesses of normal people. Accordingly the patient was never considered to be organically deteriorated nor so narcissistic as to be unreachable. The inter-psychic conflicts often originated because of childhood conflicts with parents and other early environmental factors. Thus Sullivan was desirous that nurses and attendants be sympathetic and kindly, with unlimited patience. The implications of this were far-reaching, for it is still true that in the average mental hospital the attendants, who spend more time with the patients than anyone else, are the least permanent, the least educated, the least trained, and the poorest paid on the staff. Sullivan trained his attendants and male nurses, taking several into analysis. He was their friend and they often spent many hours with him in his apartment.

With his own patients, Sullivan was the epitome of kindness, but he was not so successful in his relationship with other members of the Sheppard Pratt staff. Dr. William W. Elgin, a contemporary at the Hospital and later its Associate Medical Director, wrote that Sullivan was often in conflict with the Hospital administration, and did not work in a congenial manner with his fellows. He was difficult to deal with, had very strong likes and dislikes, and was entirely unpredictable in his relationships with other people. He could be easily irritated, sarcastic, critical, demanding, aloof, and isolated.

However Dr. Edward N. Robinson, then President of the Board, was much interested in the work of Sullivan. When he heard of Sullivan's resignation, he asked Chapman for additional information. Chapman wrote, at a later time, that Sullivan was a fine physician, a great teacher, a brilliant speaker, and an earnest and indefatigable worker, but never able to look after himself satisfactorily. He was impractical as far as his own money was concerned, and evidently "trusted the Lord to provide." Twice he owed money to the Hospital and asked the Trustees to lighten his financial burden. On the first request, the Trustees increased his salary but were unwilling to grant the second request, since a decision was made not to increase salaries further until more prosperous times returned. This was in spite of the fact that the Medical Superintendent reminded them that they were dealing with an unusual person, in unusual times, and in an unusual situation. Chapman pointed out the great value of Sullivan's work to Sheppard Pratt and the psychiatric world, and hoped that financial relief would come as a friendly gesture of appreciation. The Superintendent did not think that Sullivan's salary was worthy of his scientific achievement, but the Trustees were unwilling to change their earlier decision.

There was one other factor in Sullivan's leaving Sheppard Pratt that was not understood at the time. Sullivan expected to be given a free hand in administering the entire Reception Building, with its 75 beds, if funds could be secured. Chapman wrote to Robinson on this point: "We must not forget that there was always a question...how long we could count on him? He had never been able to adapt himself to many of the people about him. One thing that hurt him was my regretfully having to cancel plans for his taking over the administration of the Reception Building. That was quite out of the question on account of the impossibility of his cooperating with the Administrative Department.

Chapman always remained a close friend of Sullivan, fully recognized his genius, and in later years served with him on several national committees. Sullivan dedicated his first book published after leaving Sheppard Pratt to Chapman. They frequently corresponded until Sullivan's death in 1949.

During the Depression, in order that the garden, farm and dairy might make a full contribution to the

upkeep of the Hospital, J. Frank Shipley, who had been employed as a teamster in 1889, was put in charge of all outdoor operations. He had hauled much of the material used in the construction of the original buildings, using a six-man mule team, and served the Hospital for 50 years. Granville Hibberd, Manager of the Emerson Farms, was employed as consultant; an outside firm was also engaged to make a budget for the outdoor operations and arrange for an annual audit. The dairy was prospering when, in 1931, malta fever attacked the herd. The Health Department ordered the removal of 12 cows, ordered the barn to be scrubbed with soap and water followed by chloride of lime and whitewash. The barnyard was scraped and manure taken out each day. All cows purchased were tested for Bang's disease as well as tuberculosis. By 1934, the herd was clean and producing from 2,808 to 3,400 gallons of milk a month. The patients were served whole milk; employees received milk that had been hand-skimmed to secure coffee cream. On the advice of Hibberd, 74 acres of timothy hay were replaced by alfalfa. It was directed that the morning milk reach the kitchen by 7:30 AM and the evening milk by 4:30 PM. Hens produced approximately 700 eggs a day. On one occasion, Mr. Dixon noted that ice cream was purchased eight times a month at a cost of $219 and he suggested to Miss Bering that it would probably be more economical to make it at the Hospital. This shift alone resulted in a saving of over $80 a month.

The Federal Works Program Administration assisted Sheppard Pratt through these rough times by providing a horticulturist, a teacher, and a recreational leader, at no cost. Patients' spending accounts were carefully watched. On the tenth of each month, an itemized statement of each person's expenditures for the preceding month, with the balance on hand, was sent to each correspondent who signed the pa-

tient's admission blanks. If the amount was low, they were asked to add to it. Dixon suggested that each patient should keep a balance of $10 in his personal account, but the Medical Superintendent stated that this would be a heavy burden on many poor families.

But other patients ran high figures. Dixon spoke of one woman who carried $1,000 in her spending account, and the family was contacted if it fell below $250. In addition, a few families were willing to pay considerably more than the average cost, making it possible for the Hospital to increase its benevolent work. A wealthy Southerner paid $100 a week for his daughter's care, as did a Governor of one of the largest eastern states. In 1931, 6% of the patients were free, 51% paid less than the operating cost, and 43% paid more than the operating cost. In 1932, 198 out of 271 patients paid less than cost, and the total amount of benevolent work had never been so high. The following year 27% of the patients paid the full operating cost, 69% paid a portion of the cost, and 5% were free.

Now some of the small economies the Hospital took during the Depression seem rather inconsequential — such as cutting off the electricity from the elevators in the Reception Building, reducing the wattage of electric light bulbs, or hiring a man who was deaf and dumb as a painter because he would not spend so much time in conversation. But anyone who experienced the Depression will understand these steps. With all the frugality, big and little, the Hospital management was actually able to balance the accounts as early as 1935.

Sheppard Pratt remained full in spite of the scarcity of money during the Depression. The President of the Board quoted President Hoover: ''The state of affairs is due to frozen confidence. Fear has ruled the masses. They have lost confidence in themselves and those around them.'' There were,

of course, many mental breakdowns due to anxiety, fear, and worry. In 1931, admissions to Sheppard Pratt were 371, with a total number of patients treated that year of 625. This excellent census was due in part to what, at a later time, would be called good public relations. Chapman wrote: ''By telling the public what the mental institutions are doing we have an opportunity to contribute to the health and welfare of the entire country.''

Chapman spoke at many medical conventions, giving special attention to cultivating the acquaintance of physicians living south of the Mason-Dixon Line, since the largest number of families who paid the full cost came from the South, where there were few private mental institutions. He served on many committees of the Southern Medical Association and was a leading figure in its annual gatherings. He read papers at many medical and psychiatric meetings, making contact with physicians who might make referrals to Sheppard Pratt. Chapman was often seen at the Maryland Club in Baltimore, where he was well known to members of families and friends who could afford the services of the Hospital.

In spite of the Depression, papers written by members of the staff were read in medical meetings and published in various journals. Miss Madelene Ingram, Assistant Director of Nurses, wrote *Principles of Psychiatric Nurses,* a book well received by the profession. The work of Mrs. Henrietta Price brought a great deal of favorable attention to Sheppard Pratt. Price was an enthusiastic speaker, and had many opportunities to address medical gatherings both in Maryland and throughout the East. She was a regional and national officer of occupational therapy organizations. Exhibits that she arranged were taken to psychiatric meetings, and also set up in local hotel lobbies. She gave radio talks and was a frequent guest speaker before high school teachers

and PTA Associations. A movie of work done in her department was sent to Canada. Students from a dozen states came for training under her direction, from as far away as Oklahoma, Louisiana, Georgia and Canada. Visitors were legion.

Although rigid economies were practiced, Chapman reported to the Board that vital services had not suffered, and that the buildings and grounds were in good condition; necessary repairs were carried out. ''We were saved (financially),'' he said, ''through the reduction in cost of all commodities.''

In spite of the shortages of money, some improvements were made at Sheppard Pratt. There were four artesian wells on the property; one was now abandoned and deep-well pumps placed in the other three. These gave 226,000 gallons of water daily, but it proved insufficient. Brewster said the Hospital should stop sinking wells and connect with the city water supply. This was done at a cost of $25,000. The Fire Department was much pleased at this move, for there had been some uneasiness about having enough water on hand if there was a bad fire. After the connection was made, the firemen found they could shoot a stream of water over the highest roof of the Hospital, and they pronounced the buildings the best-protected in the County. Fire insurance was reduced, and a program of instruction in fire fighting, far more extensive than previously carried on, was instituted among the personnel.

One of the finest improvements was placing an elevator in the A Building, at a cost of $8,000. It was a great convenience, making it possible to place patients in some rooms formerly occupied by employees, and permitting doctors to have rooms on the fourth floor. A Cadillac automobile was purchased in 1932 and used to give patients rides into the country. Fifty-seven trips were taken that year, covering 3,896 miles!

9. Staff, Research, and Drugs

THE PSYCHIATRIC WORK at Sheppard Pratt continued on a plateau during the long depression, then moved forward. An era was coming to an end. Governor Phillips Lee Goldsborough, then a United States Senator, resigned from the Board of Trustees in 1933 after 15 years of service because of his heavy duties in Washington. John T. King, MD, Associate in Medicine and Director of the Medical Clinics at the Johns Hopkins Medical School, and later Physician-in-Chief of the 2,000 bed City Hospital, was elected to the Board in 1933. During the First World War, he was a Colonel in the Medical Corps, serving as Chief of the Medical Service of the Walter Reed Hospital. At Sheppard Pratt, he was a member of the Executive Committee, and, as Chairman through the years of the Nurses' Training Committee, gave wise counsel and was admired and regarded with affection by his associates.

William Dixon, President of the Trustees, kept in constant communication with Chapman and with Merryman, the Administrative Assistant. He knew the details of the budget, scrutinized all purchases, and reminded the administration to live within the income of the Hospital. This constant pressure placed a restriction on the Medical Superintendent. However, such close oversight enabled the Trustees not only to retain the original endowments, but to increase their capital. Dixon did not interfere with the clinical operations of the Hospital, but recognized the advantages of new activities and the need for new equipment, though he felt that changes should wait until the coming of more prosperity.

Certainly Dixon had a sense of humor. In 1935 he sent a note to Merryman, "I observe an item purchased during the month of 12 pints of red script ink...I am in hopes we can use less rather than more red ink." When a carload of Purina Chow was ordered for the dairy at an increased price, he asked the Administrative Assistant if there was not some way to reduce the quantity "of this gold dust." When beef appeared on the menu several days running, Dixon reminded the dietician that it was the best season of the year for fish, and that the Chesapeake Bay was full of blue fish.

That Dixon was a conservative businessman is indicated by his answer to a request to establish a pension system at the Hospital. He found out that the Bloomingdale Hospital was the only "sister hospital" with a pension plan, and wrote to Chapman, "I am opposed to the establishment of any system of pensions, and take the position that those who have remained long in our employ have evidently been satisfied, otherwise they would not have continued in this service, and as a large percentage of their personal care and requirements is supplied by the Hospital they would in every case be able to set aside some specific amount for the rainy day, and if they did not do that the fault lies with them, and not with us. Our job is to financially keep strong in order to carry on the Medical work and service for which the Institution was created and endowed." Yet as employees who had worked for Sheppard Pratt 30 or 40 years retired, Dixon always consented to provide them with a pension at approximately one-half their most recent salary.

There were dramatic moments, too, in the life of the Hospital. A student nurse received the thanks of the Trustees for an unusual act of bravery in risking her own life to prevent a patient's committing suicide. Miss Ann Holden was given a medal by the Trustees, and a framed certificate of appreciation. Still, there were some suicides every year. A crazed patient beat his head against the walls of the seclusion room; another patient tore off the door of a medicine cupboard and seized a bottle of carbolic acid, drinking it before a nurse could stop him;

TOP: *The Occupational Therapy staff in 1927. Mrs. Henrietta G. Price, Director, is seated third from the left.*
ABOVE: *The Windy Brae library in the 1920s.*

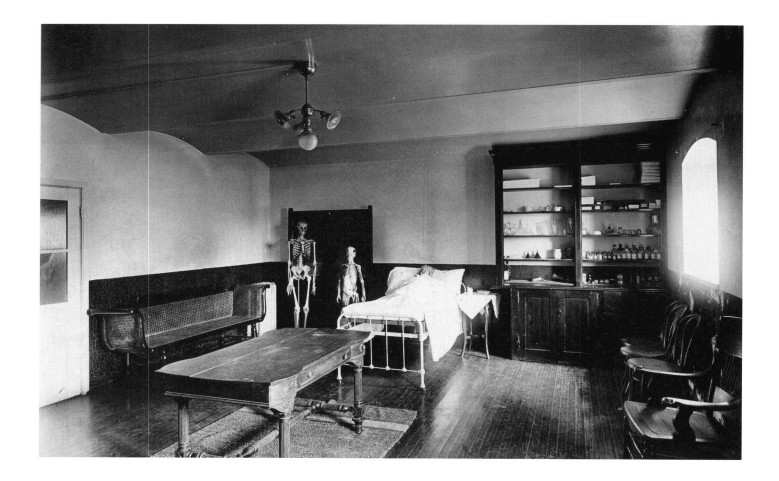

another patient drowned herself by putting her head in a toilet, and one drowned by filling a wastebasket with water! From time to time, patients would think up ingenious ways of hanging themselves. Of course, the many times when patients were prevented from committing suicide were never reported except in the nurses' notes.

Through the depression and into World War II, the Hospital was most fortunate in having a number of very able physicians on the staff. Dr. Lawrence F. Woolley came as Clinical Director in 1931 and remained until 1945. He was an excellent administrator, an exceptional clinician somewhat dogmatic and positive in his approach, but with broad vision. His papers were widely circulated.

Another well-trained, experienced physician at Sheppard Pratt during the time was Dr. Eleanore B. Saunders, who held both the MD and PhD degrees. After serving on the staff of St. Elizabeth, she spent some months in Europe in analysis. She lived for her work, and it was said of her that she was self-effacing, a delightful companion with a happy sense of humor.

Dr. Milton E. Kirkpatrick was at the Hospital from 1926 to 1930, later becoming well known in Child Guidance, holding executive administrative positions in Worcester, Massachusetts, New Orleans, and Kansas City. Dr. Douglas Noble trained at the University of Toronto and the Boston Psychopathic Hospital. A very able physician, he remained at Sheppard Pratt for ten years, leaving to go to Chestnut Lodge. Dr. Alexander R. Martin, an able, enthusiastic and energetic Irishman, was educated at Queens College in Belfast and the Royal College of Physicians and Surgeons in London. He remained at the Sheppard from 1927 to 1934, later teaching at Cornell University, the New York Hospital, and Payne Whitney Clinic. He was especially interested in finding ways to prevent young people from drifting into destructive gang behavior, and made a major contribution along this line in New York City. He published more than 50 papers, many to do with the profitable use of leisure time by young and old.

Edith H. Weigert was one of the German emigres who, fortunately for the United States, came to America because of Adolf Hitler. A graduate of the University of Berlin, she had made a sound reputation as a member of the Berlin Psychoanalytical Association, teaching in the Psychoanalytic Institute. She remained at Sheppard Pratt from 1938 to 1940, where her solid knowledge as well as her human qualities and absolute reliability were much appreciated. She spent 20 hours a week at the Hospital in psychoanalytic practice. She became Chairman of the Faculty of the Washington School of Psychiatry, and a Training Analyst in the Washington Psychoanalytic Institute. Dr. F. Temple Burling, trained at Rush Medical College in Chicago and the Los Angeles County Hospital, was at Sheppard Pratt from 1928 to 1931. He became director of several Child Guidance Clinics and then went into industrial psychiatry, first at Macy's in New York, later as Professor in the School of Industrial and Labor Relations in Cornell University. Samuel Novey, who was to give valuable service to the Hospital during several periods, was in residence from 1940 to 1942. Burling was a hard worker who later became well known in the area of child guidance and psychoanalytic techniques.

Chapman's frequent absences from the Hospital placed a heavy burden on Dr. Arthur E. Pattrell, who was both Assistant Superintendent and First Assistant Physician. He came to Sheppard Pratt in 1924, and remained until he died in 1945. "He was a fine man and physician, a highly efficient executive officer, devoted to the Hospital's welfare, possessed of excellent judgment." Pattrell was responsible

LEFT: *The nurse's classroom in the basement of the A Building. Against the wall stands the cane sofa sent as a gift to Moses Sheppard from Liberia.*
RIGHT: *Christmas mantelpiece decorations in A-4, 1930.*

for selecting patients for admission and establishing the rates. He was a steadying influence in a very difficult time.

Two physicians joined the staff in 1930 who played a major part in the growth and development of Sheppard Pratt in the decades ahead. Dr. Harry M. Murdock, who later became the third Medical Director, came to the institution in June of 1930. He was a graduate of the University of Nebraska and of its Medical School, and a Commonwealth Fellow in Psychiatry at the Colorado Psychopathic Hospital. Because of Depression conditions, Murdock was assigned for several years to give much of his time to teaching psychiatry at the University of Maryland, where he also established the psychiatric out-patient clinic. Chapman regretted this necessity, because, as he informed the Trustees, "Murdock is one of the most valuable members of our staff and his full time services are needed at the Hospital." Murdock was Chief of the Men's Service, and on leave of absence to the United States Navy during part of the Second World War, he held the rank of Commander.

Murdock was a Diplomat in Psychiatry of the American Board of Psychiatry, Chairman of the Committee on Psychiatric Nursing of the APA, and Assistant Examiner to the Board in 1942, 1946, and 1947. He was a member of the American Psychopathological Association, and its Vice-President in 1949-50; a member of the Southern Medical Association and Vice-Chairman of its Section on Neurology and Psychiatry; member of the Maryland Psychiatric Association, of which he was President in 1955 and 1956; Chairman of the Mental Hygiene Committee of the Medical and Chirurgical Faculty of Baltimore from 1953 through 1955; Chairman of the Mental Hygiene Board of Review and Director of the Mental Hygiene Society of Maryland for three years. He was an adviser to several state committees during the

Second World War, and later was a member of the medical advisory committee concerning medical care and planning for Maryland.

William Worcester Elgin received his education at Washington and Lee University and his medical degree from The Johns Hopkins University. Chapman wrote of Elgin: "He is an excellent physician, and able psychiatrist with a pleasing personality, working well with his associates. He is highly efficient and dependable." Elgin was Chief of the Women's Service from 1934 to 1946, Clinical Director from 1946-1949, Assistant Medical Director from 1949 to 1967, and Associate Medical Director from 1967 to 1970. He was a Diplomat of the Board of Psychiatry and Neurology, and a Fellow of the American Psychiatric Association. For many years he was Assistant Professor of Psychiatry at the University of Maryland. When World War II began, Chapman urged the Draft Board to excuse Elgin from Army Service as he was essential to the operation of the Hospital. "He cannot be replaced," wrote the Medical Director. Elgin built his entire professional life into Sheppard Pratt, and was rewarded by the respect and affection of his colleagues.

Dr. G. Wilson Shaffer joined the Sheppard staff as Psychologist-in-Chief the year before the Depression began and continued his services into the 1970's. He received his bachelor's degree and doctorate at the Johns Hopkins University, joining the faculty of his alma mater in 1941 as professor of psychology. He became Dean of the College of Arts and Sciences in 1942, and Dean of the University six years later. He was the first Diplomat in clinical psychology in the State of Maryland, and instrumental in founding the Maryland Psychological Association, which he served thrice as President. He was a pioneer in the development and application of principles of psychology in clinical settings in the field

LEFT: *The Casino Building under a blanket of snow.*
RIGHT: *Nurse Ludwig's room in Windy Brae.*

of abnormal psychology. He was associate editor of the *International Journal of Clinical and Mental Hypnosis,* and served on a number of State Commissions. His book, *Abnormal Psychology,* a classic in its field, went through four editions in 16 years, and has been translated into several languages and even published in Braille!

During the war period, Windy Brae was filled with student nurses, and some graduate nurses. The Administration was most fortunate in finding a wise counselor and advisor, Miss Alice Fitzgerald, who lived in the building and guided these young ladies in their personal problems from 1941 to 1948. A graduate of the Johns Hopkins School of Nursing, Fitzgerald engaged in administrative work, and when the First World War broke out she was selected as the Edith Cavell Memorial Nurse and sent to the British Army. She then served with the American Red Cross in Paris, organizing work in France and Italy. After the Armistice, Fitzgerald was appointed chief nurse of the American Red Cross in Europe, supervising nursing in Poland, Czechoslovakia, Rumania, Austria, Hungary, Yugoslavia and Albania. Following this, Fitzgerald organized the Bureau of the Red Cross in Geneva. She was advisor in nursing to the Philippine Islands, and organized the first School of Nursing in Siam. She received the Florence Nightingale Medal for meritorious service and further honors from no less than seven European countries!

Despite wartime pressures, research was never neglected at Sheppard Pratt. In February 1939 Chapman wrote in answer to a query from the American Foundation Studies in Government: "Every hospital worthy of the name must have a staff of members who are interested in special studies or special problems which engage their valuable time."

Research was all in the clinical psychiatric area.

Records were kept on a high level of completeness as regards historical material, mental findings, and laboratory tests, all of which served as a basis for research. The selection of project subjects depended on the interest and initiative of the staff physician. There was no committee on research, nor was there what would be regarded as a formal program. No research project had ever been financed by outside agencies, special gifts, or endowments used exclusively for that purpose. Necessary equipment was purchased from the general funds of the Hospital, and at least one member of the staff was designated to give most of his time exclusively to work on some subject in clinical research.

There were numerous investigative procedures conducted on individual cases that had certain special research value but did not constitute a definite program of research within the Hospital. These were selected because of the peculiar significance of the case material; those under study at the time included the relationship of inheritance to Alzheimer's disease, personality defects following prefrontal lobotomy, the incidence of psychopathic personality in marital partners, and the nature of mental illness ushered in by relapsing fever.

During the 1930's, Sheppard Pratt did a certain amount of experimenting with the use of metrazol as a convulsive treatment, as well as insulin shock treatment. Dr. Oscar Schwoerer, who trained under Dr. Manfred Sakel in Vienna, originator of this type of treatment, was brought to the Hospital to direct the process. Neither form of shock treatment was used with young people in their first attack of mental disorder, nor if the prognosis was for an illness of short duration. Its use was limited to a group of schizophrenic patients with a very poor outlook.

With consent of the family concerned, a second complete physical and laboratory examination of

the patient was given and before the process was begun the patient received an intravenous injection of sodium pentothal to prevent the sensory aura and other fear-producing experiences. These forms of treatment were used with less than 50 patients, and the staff judgment was that insulin coma might be an effective agent in altering the immediate effects of schizophrenia, but the long-term picture was not clear. In some cases its use made the patient more accessible to psychotherapy, but chlorpromazine and reserpine had a similar effect, and were cheaper and less dangerous.

When the electroconvulsive treatment equipment was purchased in 1940, the use of metrazol and insulin was dropped. Administration of shock in this form was simpler and its aftereffects far happier than with metrazol. The patient emerged from his convulsion quite happy, with no recollection of what had happened and with none of the apprehension and fear that frequently followed the earlier treatment. The electroencephalographic studies indicated that there was less actual brain disturbance incident to treatment in electric shock than in the other forms. By 1941, 60 patients were treated with electric shock, and 40% were improved and were able to go home. It was chiefly used in cases of deep psychotic depression of such severity that suicide or physical depletion might occur. There was always considerable hesitation in recommending any form of shock treatment, since no explanation could be given why it worked. Apparently there was a combination of physiologic and psychologic reaction to the convulsive treatment which produced profound changes in the ego's defense system. Whether these changes were primarily chemical, physiological or psychological was by no means clear.

As far as the records show, lobotomies were not performed at the Hospital, although they were rec-ommended to be done elsewhere in a very few cases. A number of patients who had been so treated received follow-up care at the Hospital.

A certified pharmacist was placed in charge of the drug room in 1930, and from then on new drugs that appeared from year to year, often under trade names, were dispensed. Chlorpromazine was especially helpful in those cases whose disturbances were in response to hallucinatory and delusional activities; reserpine had a tranquilizing effect on neurotic patients; the barbituric acid derivatives were sedatives and produced sleep, allaying anxiety and tension; phenobarbital and Dilantin were used in the treatment of profound disorders. After full investigation, other helpful drugs were used over the years.

The use of drugs did more to change the atmosphere of mental hospitals than any other treatment since the principles of humane care were established. The wild, screaming, unapproachable patient was now a thing of the past. Until the drugs became available, the only means possible to quiet patients was the use of wet sheet packs or hydrotherapy; now the use of chemotherapy was much easier and gave better results.

The changes brought about by drug therapy made it possible to upgrade the living conditions on the halls, and to conduct many activities not previously attempted. Seclusion rooms were still used, but there were no times when all the seclusion rooms were in use, and on occasion none was occupied. Attempts at escape were reduced, and serious attempts at suicide less frequent. With the aid of tranquilizers, many more patients could go for drives in the country, visit Towson and Baltimore for shopping excursions, with or without attendants, go to the theatre, visit art museums, take in athletic contests, and go out with relatives for dinner. Life became more varied and interesting, and improvement was advanced.

10. Trials of World War II

THE AFTERMATH OF the Great Depression was still being felt at Sheppard Pratt when war broke out in Europe in 1939. Because the future seemed obscure and full of economic problems, the Trustees were alarmed. "We may escape chaos," wrote Dixon, "but we cannot escape confusion." In a long letter to the Medical Director, he foresaw rising prices and escalated wages. With eventual development of peace there would follow depleted resources, depression, and unemployment. The President of the Board urged Chapman to practice every economy without reducing patient care. Vacancies would be left unfilled, repairs postponed, and no unnecessary equipment purchased.

While Chapman was as anxious as the Trustees to keep a balanced budget, he reminded them that the Hospital must maintain its standards of food, cleanliness, medical and nursing attention. "It is easy to destroy," he told Dixon, "but hard to build up." The Medical Superintendent felt that the average number of patients was running too high; for several years the census was 285, occasionally 300, a number that did not permit proper classification, overcrowded some areas, and interfered with adequate nursing. The amount of clerical work required of the Nursing Department had been greatly increased. When a patient was transferred from one part of the Hospital to another, the change often required moving from two to eight individuals. Checking over and arranging patients' clothing and other possessions was time-consuming. Chapman advocated keeping the census below 285 and felt that if admissions were carefully watched there need not be a decrease in total income.

Working to keep costs down, Dixon scanned the list of free patients, of whom there were 13. Of this number, four were Quakers, one a remote relation of Moses Sheppard, two former employees, one nurse, two young men working for advanced college degrees who were without funds, and three of special clinical interest. One 17-year-old boy was a ward of the Children's Aid Society, which paid his personal expenses. The illegitimate son of an insane mother, he had been placed on a farm where he spent much time daydreaming. It was feared that without treatment he would become as helpless as his mother. When he was admitted, his life's savings, amounting to $17.57, were placed in his personal account.

Among those paying a very low rate were the daughter of a poorly paid professor in a southern college, a clergyman from a small Texas town, the poor widow of a distinguished citizen, and a much beloved teacher from Knoxville, Tennessee. In 1939, the average rate for patients was $38 a week; about 46% paid more than this; and between 10% and 20% paid less, some as low as $10 a week. The highest rate was $75. There was no extra charge for individual therapy; an x-ray cost from $5 to $20, and a complete blood chemistry was $12.

Senior physicians were paid from $2,700 to $4,800, with the first $1,200 deducted as maintenance. Assistant physicians received from $1,200 to $2,700. In the Nursing Department, teaching assistants received from $1,400 to $2,100; supervising nurses from $110 to $135 a month; graduate nurses from $75 to $100 a month, and attendants from $20 to $50. All nursing personnel received maintenance.

Thus Sheppard Pratt was well organized when it entered the war period. Lines of command were carefully outlined. The Medical Superintendent employed all physicians and other officers, with department heads directly responsible to him. The First Assistant Physician, Dr. Pattrell, was available for consultation with the Superintendent, department heads and service chiefs.

Part of this organization was to keep the two sexes strictly apart. There were no women at this time in the Reception Building. When walking alone or with an attendant, men and women did not meet. This was an inheritance from the Victorian Era, and the practice was followed in all state mental hospitals. It made for an artificial situation; but this was not recognized at the time. In addition to supervising assistant physicians, the chiefs of service interviewed the families of patients on visiting days.

The organization of physicians consisted of 15 or 16 junior and senior doctors, one of whom was well trained in psychoanalytic techniques. All were engaged in the study and treatment of assigned patients in their division. Other duties included direction of the employees' clinic, night duty, and teaching nurses.

The Nursing Department was the largest department in the Hospital, with 210 employees, 170 on day duty and 40 on night. Kathleen Black, RN, and Florence H. Miller, RN, were instructors in the Training School. During the war period, there were from 47 to 70 student nurses affiliated with 10 to 12 general hospitals. Alice Yearley, RN, Day Supervisor of the Women's Division, had two assistants; Ruby Summerfield, RN, was Night Supervisor. There were 52 women attendants and 58 male attendants.

The Nursing Department included five hydrotherapy operators, two employees in the marking room, six telephone operators, four maids, three beauty parlor operators and three barbers, one housemother and her two assistants, one hostess and one porter.

There were 59 individuals working under the direction of Merryman. These included five employees in the Financial Office directed by Caroline Tesar. Alan Brown was Chief Engineer and directed the mechanical section, in which there were

three engineers, two electricians, three pipe fitters, one plumber, one laborer, one night maintenance man, one night watchman, one auto mechanic and three chauffeurs. There were three carpenters under Kemp, who was an exceptionally skilled craftsman himself, three painters, one upholsterer, and four storeroom keepers and clerks. There were 23 operators of power machinery in the laundry, and also washers and porters.

Scott Bush came to the Hospital as Farm Manager in 1941 and had oversight of his staff until 1967. Under his direction were six dairymen, two gardeners, four lawn men, and one florist.

Other employees included a pharmacist, two laboratory technicians, one x-ray operator, and a physiotherapist. These workers brought the Hospital total to 461 employees.

Dixon received complaints concerning Merryman, who was not popular with all employees. The Administrative Assistant had many difficult decisions to make, but he was invaluable to Chapman. The latter told the President, "He is an honest, conscientious and faithful servant of the Hospital. His job requires both diplomacy and tact in handling different personalities; his job is a taxing one, and if he is not popular — as some claim — few were popular in such a position, since he carries out the decisions made by the administration."

Along with their Hospital duties, Drs. Chapman, Woolley, Murdock and Elgin also taught psychiatry at the University of Maryland. During much of the war period, Murdock allotted half of his time to the University, where he made an important contribution in the medical and surgical wards. "His...record of accomplishment is one of which we can be proud," reported the Medical Superintendent. Chapman added: "There has been a great change in medical education in the past few years, for which

psychiatry is largely responsible. That subject has come to take a more important place in the curriculum of all Class-A medical schools."

As munition orders from Europe flooded the country and American defenses increased, the labor situation changed rapidly. Instead of twelve million unemployed as in 1932, by 1940 there were practically none. Large numbers of women entered the labor market for the first time. By 1939 Sheppard Pratt began to lose maintenance men, dietary and laundry personnel and attendants. The turnover in attendants has always been an index of economic conditions. In some cases attendants left the Hospital for more remunerative work.

There was also great restlessness among the nursing staff, as all over the country nurses migrated from one institution to another. Many who sought shelter during the Depression in hospitals now took up private duty nursing or went into industry. All were seeking work with an eight-hour day, while at Sheppard Pratt the night shift was still on an eleven and a half hour program, six nights a week. If the Hospital moved to an eight hour day it would require the addition of 25 nurses who, even if they could be obtained, would now command a much higher salary scale. Miss Belyea reported to Chapman: "The longer we wait to go on an eight-hour day, the harder it will be to catch up. The likelihood of securing desirable nurses grows less every year. Nurses, like other people, are demanding time to live their private lives. They need time from the morbidity of a sick environment to strengthen their reserves and refresh their outlook on life, which at best is fraught with conflict and uncertainty."

With the entry of the United States into the war, Sheppard Pratt entered its most difficult period. Nothing could be done to stop the flow of personnel away from the Hospital. Farm, maintenance,

LEFT: *The carpentry shop was located in the basement of B Building.*

RIGHT: *On November 18, 1929 the Hospital converted from coal to oil as its main source of fuel. Here the new tank has just been delivered and is about to be lowered into the ground. Henry Koch and Frank Shipley supervise at the far right of the picture.*

dietary workers and attendants were drawn into munitions industries or were drafted. Within a year, most of this group had left. In addition, the quality of attendants rapidly deteriorated. The administration could never tell from day to day who would be on hand to work. New recruits were alcoholics, decrepits, down-and-outers who were here today and gone tomorrow; even a few parolees from the Federal prison were tried. Men who had been at the Hospital for years left on a few hours notice. Even raising wages had little effect.

Miss Belyea reported that conditions were becoming appalling. "Nerves fray easily," she said, "patience grows thin and fatigue shows...it is a time of improvising, temporizing, bolstering of weak places." Care of the patients was made possible only by the presence of student nurses whose numbers increased during this period. They were on duty 52 to 54 hours a week; their classes were accelerated, and their term of training was cut from 36 weeks to 30, and finally to 24. Seminars were replaced by ward clinics where the patient was seen, his participation enlisted, behavior noted, and then his needs discussed. Dr. Shaffer was of great assistance, giving 12 to 16 lectures on psychology to each group of nurses in training. Over the weekends, students from Towson Normal School and Johns Hopkins were secured as attendants, and these groups were enlarged in the summer months by students from Emory University and Vanderbilt University.

Twelve rooms were opened on the third floors of the A and B Buildings for graduate nurses, but many of these did not wish to live in, and transportation was difficult because of gas rationing. More female nurses were placed on male halls, but there were times when there was not a single graduate nurse on a hall. Attendants were required to spend several hours a day in the Dietary Department and so were diverted from care of patients. For some months, there were four attendants on a hall that normally had a quota of 30. The Occupational Therapy Department loaned some of its workers for hall duty. Soon changes had to be made in admissions; fewer violent patients were accepted; and elderly individuals who required extra nursing were discharged. By 1942 halls were gradually closed and the patient census cut from 285 in 1942 to 260. Finally in 1944 it was necessary to close to patients the Reception Building with its 85 beds.

Fortunately for the Hospital its leading doctors, Pattrell, Woolley, Murdock and Elgin, had all refused flattering offers to go elsewhere, and few of the senior physicians were called into service. Dr. Chapman reported to the Trustees that he was holding on to his experienced physicians. "We are strong at present," he wrote. "I do not know when I will have to weaken the staff. If I ever have to tear down our medical staff, or rather skeletonize it, I would like to have as strong a framework on which to rebuild as it is possible for me to have."

Soon the armed services began to call the younger physicians. Doctors Ingalls, Jarvis and Page went into the Army, Pembroke into the Navy. Murdock himself was on active duty in the Navy 1943-1946. In his absence, Elgin served as Chief of Service for both women's and men's divisions. Returning to Baltimore to enter private practice, Dr. Samuel Novey still rendered Sheppard Pratt valuable service.

With the shortage of maids and dietary help, patients were asked to assist in their places. Soon 47 patients were working in the kitchens and dining rooms with evident delight. A former patient's family wrote to Pattrell: "From the day Mother started to work in the kitchen, I began to see an improvement in her, over and above what would be normally expected...Mother had made a thousand bracelets

LEFT: *The "stained glass" of this play-set was made by patients with colored tissue paper.*
RIGHT: *Dramatic productions by patients were highly regarded for both their therapeutic and entertainment values.*

and a thousand wooden boxes and a hundred leather belts, and rather than helping her, they made her feel doubly useless and made her realize her remoteness from normal existence. But working in the kitchen was interesting because for the first time she was actually doing something of real value, and secondly, because the running of such a kitchen is an interesting operation." Experiences like these during the war foreshadowed the work program later developed at the Hospital.

Bering reported that she made out menus though they were practically useless since she never knew from day to day what supplies would be available. There were times when the Hospital had no meat for several days running. The Price Administration notified the Hospital that when they butchered their own cattle they would have to deduct one and one-half red points from the rationing allowance for each pound of beef secured. Miss Tesar of the Financial Department reported that for the first time at Sheppard Pratt she counted in millions — coupons, not money. In spite of all the difficulty, food was substantial and in sufficient quantities. Chapman wrote to Bartlett: "The Dietary Department carries on remarkably well, thanks to the physical strength and the everlasting drive and energy of Miss Bering. He added, "She has done extensive canning, particularly of tomatoes, of which we raised more than we could use. She has been on many days, up at six in the morning and has not retired before half past twelve or one o'clock at night."

Often the Hospital appealed to the State Committee on Procurement and Assignment to retain workers for certain crucial positions, but, with the exception of engineers, none was allowed to remain. On one occasion, a cook "frozen" in his position came to Dr. Chapman and said, "Please, sir, I have another job, and want to be thawed out."

When blackouts were ordered and air raid warnings given, personnel and staff reported immediately to assigned posts, nurses and attendants to their halls. With the pulling of three switches, all lights in the main buildings could be put out. Flashlights were used by the staff, and usually a complete blackout only lasted a moment, followed by a dim-out. A trunk line was set aside on the switchboard to receive warnings of airplane raids. The plan was to have ten whistles blown when enemy planes were within 100 miles. Large red crosses were painted on the roofs of all major buildings, and aviators from the nearby Curtis-Wright airfield reported that they could distinguish the marks plainly at an elevation of 5,000 feet.

New interest in the Occupational Therapy Department was created by making garments for relief agencies. In 1943 for example, 2,555 garments were made, including 302 for the Red Cross, 170 for the Children's Aid Society, and 99 for British Relief. In addition, 2,740 surgical dressings were made and 100 metal splints. Later the number of articles made in a single year reached 5,000. Bedspreads were crocheted and raffled at $110; the money was given to the British Refugee Children's Fund.

Several members of the Nursing Department taught courses in First Aid, Home Hygiene, Care of the Sick at Home, and Advanced First Aid in nearby churches. Miss Frey, RN, was a member of the County War Council; Miss Miller, RN, a manager of the Women's Motor Corps. On Sheppard Pratt's service flag were 52 stars.

Some gains were achieved during the war period. The American Medical Association and the American Board of Psychiatry and Neurology renewed the certification of The Sheppard and Enoch Pratt Hospital as a teaching hospital. Previously, some of the courses required for residency training were

given outside Sheppard Pratt; now these were transferred to the Hospital. In 1944 the National League for Nursing Education accredited Sheppard Pratt's Nursing Training program.

At the same time, regulations covering parole of patients were standardized. Before a patient went back into the outside world, it seemed wise to the staff that some preliminary steps be taken. Sometimes this was done by assigning patients to work in the Hospital of a useful nature, and noting how well they carried out their responsibilities. The areas most used were housekeeping, dietary, secretary pool, maintenance, and nursing. The patient was asked to work three hours a day, five days a week, either in the morning or afternoon. Assignments were made on the suggestion of the individual's physician, on consulting with the Chief of Service and the department head. After the assignment was made, the Director of Occupational Therapy took charge, reporting on the quality of the work accomplished. In time the patient was allowed to go home or elsewhere as arranged for a weekend. His room was held and the family was expected to pay the usual rate for the period. If the patient was placed on parole for a longer period, his case was reviewed after two or three weeks and then he was discharged or returned to Sheppard Pratt. If return was necessary, no further routine admission examinations were required.

Extra precautions were taken during the war period to prevent fires. Careful plans had been maintained for years with a fire crew of 30 or 40 men responding quickly to each alarm. Fire drills were conducted twice each month, always with one fire hydrant turned on in rotation. Six or seven lengths of fire hose were used and also rotated. Water at 60 to 80 pounds pressure could be forced through the whole Hospital system, pumping 300 gallons a minute. In addition, the city water system, with a greater pressure, could be added.

The Trustees were most appreciative of the outstanding work of the staff during the difficult war days. Chapman, "who was an inspiration to the whole," was warmly commended, as well as Belyea, Director of Nurses and Miss Bering, Chief Dietician.

In the spring of 1945, Chapman completed his 25th year as Medical Superintendent. A testimonial dinner was tendered him by the Trustees, marked by a silver tray suitably inscribed, and an appropriate resolution placed in the Trustees' minutes, which declared that the Medical Superintendent had "served this Institution with diligence and distinction, bringing to it outstanding medical leadership and administrative ability," and that under his guidance "it had grown and prospered and has expanded the beneficent work for which it was organized." With this gift, the Board members recorded their deep feeling of gratitude for Chapman and their confidence in the continued success of his administration.

The Trustees had planned an appropriate series of exercises to mark the 50th anniversary of the opening of The Sheppard and Enoch Pratt Hospital, which took place on November 29th, 1941. It was expected that Mr. Dixon would preside, but unfortunately he died a few days before the exercises were held. Dixon was elected a Trustee in 1916 and became President in 1930. He always had "a keen interest in the welfare of the Institution, as well as faithfully serving its best interests by applying unstintedly of his valuable time; his sound judgement and his sincere human sympathies" were highly esteemed by the members of the Board. A second heavy loss in the same year was that of Benjamin H. Brewster, Vice-President of the Trustees, who served "for 14 years with outstanding efficiency," most of that period as Chairman of the Farm Committee.

11. Postwar Problems

J. KEMP BARTLETT, Jr. eighth President of the Board of Trustees, summed up the end-of-the-war conditions in a letter to his fellow Trustees on September 25, 1945. "As you know, for more than three years war conditions mainly manifested themselves in shortages of all classifications of professional services, labor and materials, and has greatly influenced each decision which we have had to make with respect to the operation of the Hospital. During that time we have endeavored to render the same degree of professional treatment, care and maintenance as...in the past. It has been necessary to limit the number of patients admitted and to curtail our...operations in other respects."

The first move Bartlett considered necessary was to reopen the Reception Building, possible only when sufficient psychiatrists, nurses, attendants and maintenance men could be secured. He realized that a great deal of repair work and a thorough renovation of the Reception Building were necessary before this structure, normally housing one-third of the patients, could be placed in service. Walls had been moisture-damaged, paint had peeled, floors had buckled, and the furniture was worn and drab.

In the war's aftermath, Chapman was certain of the long-time need of psychiatrists. Between the end of the First World War and the Second, the government had spent more than a billion dollars on service-connected psychiatric disabilities. Three out of every five beds in the 79 Veterans Administration Hospitals were occupied by patients with nervous and mental disorders. The armed forces of the United States in the Second World War were nearly triple those of the First, and the psychiatric casualties were approximately in the same proportion. Many psychiatrists would be needed to give them proper treatment.

Chapman indicated to the Trustees that more graduates of medical schools would desire further instruction in psychiatry, following their residency in a general hospital. The only place this training could be secured was in a mental hospital equipped and accredited for such instruction, as Sheppard Pratt was. Many physicians, following their Army duty, were asking for psychiatric training; and the need for psychiatric nurses was very great. Psychiatry as a branch of medicine was entering general education, business, industry, religion, sociology, and penology. To Chapman, this trend indicated that The Sheppard and Enoch Pratt Hospital would have opportunities and responsibilities to an extent not equaled before. In addition, research programs should increase.

Although expanding opportunities lay ahead, Chapman reminded the Trustees that the quality of work at Sheppard Pratt was at a low ebb because of the war conditions, general feelings of insecurity, and depletion of the nursing service. Fully aware of the necessity of living within the Hospital's budget, he felt that the benevolent work desired by Moses Sheppard should continue. After the necessary renovations, he hoped the work of the Hospital could be expanded, especially in services rendered to young people. He suggested that the benevolent funds be devoted largely to their care and treatment.

Dr. Chapman mentioned that he had heard some "casual conversation" to the effect that future real estate values might make it undesirable for Sheppard Pratt to retain its present site, but wisely remarked, "I cannot let myself get confused as to such a possibility. It will be a long time and the Hospital should, during that period of years, enhance its standing in medicine and education, and I hope add to its endowment funds materially so that its future on this or another site will be bright."

The first task following the war was to renovate the Reception Building and improve the patients'

ABOVE: Woodshop tasks included cutting bases to be used in basket weaving therapy.

LEFT: Serving well-balanced and appetizing meals was difficult in wartime. The farming operation of the Hospital was a necessity. Milk, beef, pork, potatoes, corn, soy beans, and wheat as well as other crops were produced on the grounds.

halls. Chapman wanted the Reception Building to receive all patients for physical and mental examinations as originally designed. Minor changes were made in the two older buildings, the kitchens and cafeteria were enlarged, and patient rooms refurnished, as at the present time there was a strange mixture of ancient and modern furniture. Attention needed to be given to the heating plant, which was 50 years old, and operating in a wasteful and uneconomical manner.

Then, although this would require from one-quarter to one-third more staff, the Nursing Department, Chapman stated, should be placed on an eight-hour day. Members of this department should be permitted to live off-grounds, a privilege not granted before, with the Hospital furnishing transportation to the nearest trolley line on York Road. He also suggested some form of group insurance.

During the war, the Trustees rented three houses for physicians in nearby Towson, and the Medical Superintendent advocated construction of houses on the property for at least three staff members. But Chapman had more ambitious plans, and asked the Board to consider the building of an interdenominational chapel, a recreation building, a swimming pool, and a centralized building for occupational therapy. Considering the rows of staff automobiles parked on Hospital roads unsightly, Chapman suggested that a three-story garage be built on the sloping ground near the power plant, with the top floor devoted to rooms for porters. Since every foot of the A and B Buildings was filled "with a disgraceful huddle of activities, to which the staff was by way of becoming habituated," and the medical records were housed in the basement, Chapman advocated the erection of a new administration building. This could be placed between the A and B Buildings in front of the service building, which Chapman said,

"could hardly be considered a thing of beauty."

The Trustees were much taken by Chapman's ideas concerning an expanded program. They employed a Baltimore architect, James R. Edmunds, Jr., to submit preliminary plans for the various structures. Edmunds began his task at once, and within a few months submitted designs for all the buildings suggested by Chapman. The architect's plans were carefully studied, but no action was taken because of continued unsettled conditions. And the years immediately following the war were no easier than the war years.

The only building erected under the guidance of Edmunds was not even listed in his original set of designs; this was a pasteurizing plant, long advocated by Dr. John T. King and strongly recommended by the Health Department. It was built in 1946 at a cost of approximately $20,600. This building, of glazed brick, was connected with the barn by a short covered passageway. Modern pasteurizing and bottling equipment was installed, and ten gross of quart bottles, two gross of pints, and 15 gross of one-half pint square bottles purchased. Individuals were served one-half pint bottles in the dining rooms, and each patient was allotted one quart of milk a day. A different colored cap was used to designate the morning and evening supply of milk.

The dairy herd produced plenty of milk for patients, staff and employees; there was even a significant overabundance, and the extra supply was fed to the pigs. Usually the herd consisted of 50 to 60 milkcows, 14 to 16 heifers, 18 to 20 calves, and two bulls, with as many as 15 to 30 steers. In the piggery, there were 80 to 100 pigs and 20 to 30 shoats. Steers were slaughtered for Hospital use when they weighed approximately 600 pounds. Pork was supplied in large quantities to the kitchens, while hams and bacon were cured for later use. Potatoes proved to be

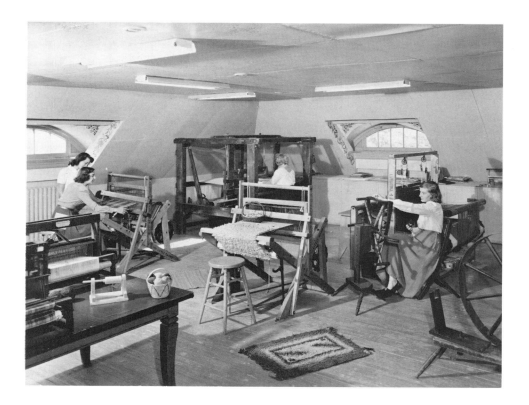

LEFT: *The Casino was the site of many recreational activities.*
RIGHT: *Occupational therapy for women included weaving.*
BELOW: *Woodworking was considered men's work.*

a very valuable crop, with from 800 to 1,200 bushels brought in each fall by a mechanical digger. One silo was filled with hay and one with alfalfa. Ten acres of corn were normally planted each spring, several acres of wheat, and considerable soy beans.

Chapman felt that the time had come to establish a Children's Division at Sheppard Pratt. This desire grew out of various experiments the Hospital had made with Children's Clinics. In the 1920's, clinics were established in various counties of the State; and for many years physicians from Sheppard Pratt went weekly to clinics in Baltimore, Cecil, Queen Anne, and Kent Counties. As early as 1927, there is a long report in the Hospital records summarizing the examinations of 44 children and interviews with their parents. The ages ranged from an eight-month-old baby to a girl of 20 years.

In the 1930's, two physicians and a psychologist from Sheppard Pratt visited the four county clinics, assisting the health officers with special-problem young people. They also provided consultation for the Baltimore County Circuit Court on juvenile delinquency. In 1937, Chapman was appointed by Governor Nice as a member of a Commission to study special-problem children, as well as feeble-minded and insane ones.

Dr. Alexander Martin of Sheppard Pratt's staff had been much interested in working with children, and later Dr. Samuel Novey, a Resident and later Assistant Psychiatrist, conducted a Children's Clinic at Sheppard Pratt. This followed a request of the Baltimore County Children's Aid Society and the Juvenile Court. For several years, Novey came to the Hospital two mornings a week and saw children referred by both agencies. He examined these children and gave a written opinion to the referring agency. Contrary to expectations, however, the clinic did not grow, probably because it was not set up to

give treatment. This would have taken a great deal of time and would have been relatively expensive. Nevertheless in 1947 the Children's Aid Society provided $300 per year as part payment on the salary of a psychologist, and the Juvenile Court did likewise. The Hospital supplied Novey with social service, office space, and secretarial help. Useful work was carried on for several years.

Chapman had more ambitious plans, however. He advocated that a Children's Division should be established in which psychiatrists, psychologists, and social workers could examine and treat children with incipient mental disorders. He envisioned a school with 28 to 40 beds, a staff of its own, and space enough for classrooms, play rooms, examination rooms, offices, dining and kitchen facilities. He believed that such a division could be of tremendous service to the community, and that in a few years it would be self-supporting. He had interviewed a wealthy family, which seemed much interested in the project and gave ''semiassurance'' that they would make a substantial contribution towards the maintenance of such a program.

On the east side of the Hospital property lay a 25 acre tract, known as Kenaway, on which there was a large, three-story house built in the Federal period, thought to have been designed by the architect of the famous Hampton Mansion. Learning that this property was coming on the market, the Trustees purchased it for the sum of $21,860.05. At the time, it was planned that as soon as the war was over, a capable staff should be secured to operate a new division. A staff committee consisting of Dr. Wilson Shaffer, Dr. Woolley, Dr. Novey, Herbert M. Taylor and Philip E. Lamb, was appointed to work with the Medical Superintendent. Two of the Trustees were to help carry forward the plan.

In 1947, the Ivy Nook, a tea and gift shop, was opened in the B Building for the use of patients, their families, and employees. This proved to be a very pleasant spot for sociability, and the patients welcomed the opportunity to purchase light refreshments between meals. Bartlett even instituted a Fishing Club, first mentioned in 1946. This social group provided an opportunity for employees to become acquainted with staff and Trustees. It was a real morale-builder during the trying period after the war, and continued for several decades with such pleasant social events as crab feasts, shrimp feasts, and bingo. Each year the fish pond on the property was stocked by the Hospital for the Fishing Club.

As soon as the war was over, many of the physicians came back to Sheppard Pratt, where they were joined each quarter by four residents sent by the University of Maryland Medical School for advanced training. In addition, the United States Public Health Bureau granted stipends of $3,500 yearly for doctors who had been in the services in taking up psychiatric training. A number came to Sheppard Pratt over the next few years.

Unfortunately the nurses did not return to Sheppard Pratt as the physicians did. In 1946 the Hospital was short 100 nurses and attendants in Miss Belyea's department. Belyea reported that nurses disliked the nonprofessional tasks they were required to perform. She pointed out, ''The lack of appreciation of what the position of a nurse should be in the care and treatment of patients; the feeling on the part of the nurse that she should be more closely related, both in her educational opportunities and professional labors, with the medical profession point to the fact that she desires a place of greater dignity than she feels she now occupies.''

Still, many nurses desired to continue their studies toward a BS or MS degree, and at that time there was no nearby institution of higher learning to which

a Sheppard Pratt nurse could go for part-time work. Fortunately for the Nursing Department, there was an unusually strong group of instructors available to teach the enlarged body of student nurses on whom the Hospital chiefly depended. Lavour Miller, RN, was Senior Instructor and Assistant to Belyea; Betty Leitch, RN, was Clinical Ward Instructor; while Anna G. Hartley, RN, and Estelle Thompson, RN, were exceptional Day Supervisors. Ruby Summerfield, RN, who came to the Hospital in 1931, was asked to be Night Supervisor.

Each year Sheppard Pratt enrolled in its Student Nurses' Program approximately 300 young women, who came for from seven to 13 weeks during their second or third year of training. Their curriculum included 60 hours of instruction in nervous and mental disease — including clinical nursing; five hours of conferences on ward practice, a correlation of psychiatric and general nursing; 15 hours of practical nursing administration; 15 hours of occupational therapy; 15 hours of instruction in hydrotherapy; 20 hours of social work; five hours in the use of the library; 15 hours of sociology; and 15 hours in educational psychology. The postgraduate instruction of nurses, which had begun in 1905, was phased out during the war from lack of applicants, and nearly 300 RNs had completed this advanced training at the Hospital by then.

In the summer, girls from Seton Hall College and Pennsylvania State College assisted on the convalescent halls. Belyea told the Medical Director that she would remain in her post until the end of the war. When retired in 1946, she was warmly thanked for "her untiring efforts and loyalty to nursing and nursing education."

A year later Margaret E. Newcomb, RN, was appointed to take her place. Newcomb had attended the University of Colorado for three years before entering its School of Nursing. She was a highly intelligent person and extremely able. Her predecessor described her as "trim, attractive...and socially acceptable." Newcomb demonstrated her quick wit and stamina on a later occasion when the Stratocruiser on which she was returning from Japan crashed in Puget Sound. Removing her shoes, which would become water-logged, she tossed the foam rubber seat cushions out to the passengers to use when the plane sank. Although five passengers drowned in the cold April waters of the Sound, all the rest survived.

Arthur E. Pattrell, First Assistant Physician and Assistant Superintendent, died after a long illness on December 17, 1945. Chapman wrote of Pattrell: "He was a fine man and physician, a highly efficient executive officer, devoted to the welfare of the hospital, and possessed of excellent judgment. He will be greatly missed." During the war he had carried many of the duties normally undertaken by the Medical Superintendent. Chapman reported to the Trustees: "For the time being, Dr. Elgin is taking Dr. Pattrell's place, and is doing very well...Dr. Elgin has been a tower of strength during the past four or five years." It was planned that Dr. Murdock, when released from the Navy, would take over the services performed by Pattrell.

But early in 1947, Chapman underwent a severe operation. He returned briefly to take his place at the Hospital, but died on September 24, 1948.

And so a giant departed. "He carried the Hospital on through many difficult times, including the greatest depression this country has ever seen, and a war which has depleted the country's resources and left behind serious problems. He was a source of inspiration to all of us," wrote Mr. Bartlett. "His advice and kindly sympathetic counsel did much to maintain a high level of morale."

12. A Teaching Institution

DURING MOST OF the last two years of Dr. Chapman's life, Dr. Murdock had acted as Medical Superintendent, and it had been a difficult time for him. Expenditures were higher than income, and the Hospital lost approximately $2,000 a month. Members of the Hospital Committee met with Murdock each week to check the cost of supplies and to consider individual rates. Much of the increase in cost was due to the arrival of equipment ordered during the war but not delivered, and to the rising cost of materials needed to carry out necessary repairs. In addition, food and labor costs sky-rocketed. Where possible the Committee raised rates, the standard charge now being placed at $75 a week. Some wondered if Sheppard Pratt would price itself out of the market.

In April of 1949, Murdock was appointed executive head with the new title of Medical Director. He was an obvious choice to succeed Chapman. Murdock's experience had been broadened by the period spent in the Navy, and his familiarity with all departments in the Hospital increased during Chapman's illness. He was certainly well-groomed for this larger task, and the Hospital needed a strong executive.

The previous year there had been a deficit of over $100,000 in operating costs; and there were still 85 empty beds. Wages and salaries could not be reduced, but department heads were required to cut their employees by ten percent. Salaries and wages took 69 percent of the income from patients, yet these expenses were far below the wages that industry was paying, or that nurses and attendants in general hospitals or institutions managed by the Veterans Bureau received.

Bright spots included the continued support of the Veterans Bureau, which paid the full cost for several patients; the willingness of the Public Health Service to provide four residents a year; and the University of Maryland, which continued to send three resident physicians each quarter for further training. The Trustees agreed to create a new position, Physician-in-Chief, to be filled by a physician of high qualifications and experience in the field of psychiatry. His duties were to be entirely clinical without the burden of administrative responsibility.

Within a short period, Murdock was appointed a Fellow in the Southern Psychiatric Association, an Assistant Professor at the University of Maryland, and, by Governor Lane, a member of the Mental Hygiene Board of Review, and placed on the Board of Directors of the Maryland Mental Hygiene Society.

In 1949 the new Medical Director laid before the Trustees several important matters for their decision. He wrote: ''The fundamental situation which must be considered and decided, and upon which everything else depends, must be a thoughtful and mature decision as to the future course and direction which your hospital is to take. If we are to continue to exist it must be along one of two roads. We must either resume the honored place which we have previously held, or we must resign ourselves to thinking purely in terms of offering competent care and so sink into comfortable mediocrity.'' The primary need, Murdock wrote, was the presence at the Hospital ''of one or two outstanding therapists — physicians who are universally acknowledged to be masters in the treatment and understanding of patients and whose time can be devoted entirely to that end, and to the instruction of physicians who come here for training. Their freedom to function as therapists is the primary consideration.'' Murdock warned the Trustees that such experts would be expensive, but had confidence that if they were secured, sufficient patients would wish to come to the Hospital to fill the beds which had long been vacant. He urged the Trustees to put less emphasis

on balancing the budget and more on the primary humane concerns of the Founder "to carry forward and improve the ameliorated system of treatment of the insane."

Shortly after his appointment, Murdock submitted to the Trustees a reorganization plan, plus an outline of the duties of various personnel, the first such document in the records. At the top was the Medical Director, the administrative head of the Hospital. Close to the Medical Director was a new official, Psychiatrist-in-Chief or Director of Therapy. This was to be a man of prolonged and varied experience in all the accepted methods of treatment, who could demonstrate and relate these methods to individual cases. His duties were to include intensive, individual treatment of a limited number of patients; the explanation and demonstration of treatment to other members of the staff, the intermediate and training groups; individual discussion with other members of the staff concerning patient problems; research into various aspects of treatment; and stimulation of such research by others.

The Assistant Medical Director, Dr. William W. Elgin, was the executive officer of the Hospital. His duties included scheduling and admitting new patients, and association with their families; checking and supervising the management of the wards; handling the financial details of patients' accounts and expenditures; advising the Chiefs of Service; acting as the coordinator of internal Hospital activities; supervising fire drills and safety measures; handling legal problems concerning patients; and acting for the Medical Director in his absence.

The Clinical Director, Dr. Frederic G. Worden, was charged with the duty of maintaining the highest professional standards of care and treatment on the wards, by constant observation and checking on the care of patients and all their activities. He had super-

TOP: *The Board of Trustees in 1934 included: President William A. Dixon , Philips Lee Goldsborough, Robert H. Walker, Auston McLanahan, Benjamin H. Brewster, III, T. Stockton Matthews, J. Kemp Bartlett, Jr. and John T. King MD.*
ABOVE: *A typical day in the Hospital's laboratory, located in the B Building basement.*

ABOVE: *The Sheppard and Enoch Pratt Orchestra — several of its members were occupational therapists.* BELOW: *Under the direction of newly appointed Psychiatrist-in-Chief, Lewis Brown Hill MD, nurses review patient folders.*

vision over the professional activities of physicians, nurses, occupational therapists, and attendants.

The Chiefs of Service were responsible for individual admissions, assigning patients to wards, and transferring them from ward to ward when desirable. These officials were responsible for all protective and restraining measures, for the care and management of patients, tending to their supplies, their mail, and rendering information when proper to outside sources, such as relatives or physicians. They gave administrative supervision to residents working on their wards.

Murdock's organizational chart called for two Chiefs of Service and seven physicians, two on the intermediate level, and two to five residents in training. If the census rose above 200, another physician would be needed for each 20 additional patients. Through his period as administrator, Murdock was most successful in judging the caliber and capabilities of physicians, and securing their interest in the Hospital. One of the most important and successful of all his appointments made in 1949 was that of Lewis Brown Hill as Psychiatrist-in-Chief. He had served as Clinical Director at Sheppard Pratt from 1929 to 1931.

Hill had a magnetic attraction that turned everyone toward him. He took an intense interest in each patient, noted what each one said or did, knew what they were doing and what they were likely to do. His treatment and goals were realistic, and his expectations for patients never went beyond their potential capacity. He thought of each one as a person, not as an interesting study in psychopathology.

Hill had much to do with establishing a systematic training program for assistant physicians. At Sheppard Pratt, as in most mental hospitals at the time, formal courses of training were just beginning. Usually the new physician, once given a list of pa-

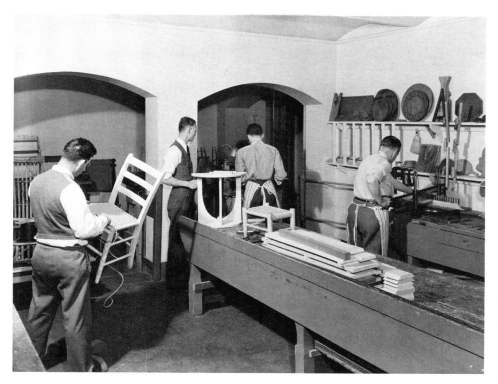

LEFT: *Wood shop: "Occupational therapy is to be regarded as a valuable part of any institutional program in that it prevents the outcropping of those serious characteristics which will appear in any group of men who are unoccupied and without interesting activity," Dr. Hill on the value of occupational therapy.*

tients, was more or less on his own. The incoming assistants were usually unmarried and lived in staff quarters. Each morning they met the Clinical Director, with whom methods of treatment were discussed and advice given. At meal times and in their apartments, the new assistants discussed their experiences, and spent much time in contact with each other and reading in the medical library. Information was secured chiefly through study and skills by a process of experience and what "rubbed off."

Hill advocated greater use of social workers, who he thought were able to secure important information not revealed to the therapist from the families of patients. It was not the duty of the Hospital to treat the patient's relatives, nor to teach them psychology, but the social worker could interpret the therapist to the family and the family to the therapist.

Hill also had great faith in the value of occupational therapy. From his experiences in state hospitals, where many patients could not enter into recreational or occupational therapy, he came to believe that "restraints and seclusion which we regarded as necessary because of the violence of the patients, was in fact responsible for the violence...The capacity and need for work is one of the distinguishing characteristics of the human as opposed to the animal...occupational therapy is a valuable part of any institutional program in that it prevents the outcropping of those serious characteristics which will appear in any group of men who are unoccupied and without interesting activity."

In Hill's day, there were two services at the Hospital. One, the continued care service, was made up of those patients who were considered unable to use intensive psychotherapy. The other, the acute service, included all patients on admission, all patients with acute mental illness and all who were considered likely to be able to make use of intensive

psychotherapy. Each resident physician was assigned to both male and female patients and worked with his patient as he moved from ward to ward. The Psychiatrist-in-Chief and Clinical Director, who were responsible for the quality of psychotherapy and of training, entered into the "rounds." The senior psychiatrist visited the patient assigned to the resident scheduled for rounds that day. Each patient was given an opportunity to express his thoughts, preoccupations, and questions. The visit took place without interrupting the patient's schedule, and might take place on the ward, in hydrotherapy or in occupational therapy. The senior psychiatrist asked questions, answered questions, and suggested lines of discussion which might be taken up with the resident. The patient might consider these visits as an unwelcome intrusion into his relationship with the resident, as an opportunity to complain, or as complementing his contact with the resident.

Hill reorganized the staff conferences on Friday mornings, endeavoring to make them more worthwhile. He sent around a memo stating that this period would be devoted to the presentation of one case. The main objective would be to furnish material for a discussion of principles of psychotherapy in various types of psychiatric illnesses, and to facilitate participation by the staff in the planning of further treatment for the patient being presented. It was planned that the patients discussed would be those presenting problems in psychotherapy rather than those with organic difficulties. He instructed the residents to choose patients who had been at the Hospital from four to six weeks, evaluate the meaning of their illnesses, the probable therapeutic goals, and the possible techniques for assisting the patient to reach these goals. Another type to be discussed would be those whose therapy was almost terminated when there was a problem of how to make

LEFT: *Nurses and patients enjoy a game of volleyball while another solitary soul enjoys the view of the fields.*
BELOW LEFT: *Excerpt from "Windfalls," the student nurses' publication of the '30s and '40s.*
RIGHT: *The ground floor east entrance of the Chapman Building.*

SHEPPARD PRATT HOSPITAL

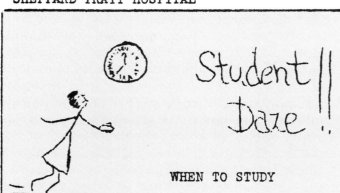

WHEN TO STUDY

Don't study when you're happy
Don't study when you're blue
Don't study when you're tired
Or have something else to do,

Don't study in the morning
'Cause that's the time for work,
Don't study in the afternoon
You gotta rest, you jerk!

Don't study in the evening
Go on and keep the date,
Don't study after 10 o'clock
Lights should be off that late,

Don't study on your day off
Relaxing's too darn swell,
But every other time it's best
To study just like h--l.

                              S.B.G.

the breaking-off most helpful to the patient's future adjustment outside the Hospital. A third type would be those in whom therapy was blocked, and the physician was bored, puzzled, angry, or anxious.

The conferences were to be assigned in rotation, the physician being free to choose which patient he wished to discuss, securing approval from the Clinical Director in advance. Hill noted that there was nothing so profitless as sitting through a poor conference, and advised the residents to prepare well in advance, to study their notes carefully, and to make concise outlines of the material to be presented. He warned that if they left themselves entirely out of the presentation, the meaning of the data would be lost, for a psychiatric illness was a disorder in interpersonal relationships. The most observable and vivid manifestation of the disorder would be shown in the conversations of both patient and doctor. If the resident left the patient out of his presentation his audience could not see the reaction pattern in the patient's life. History and descriptions of events were only valuable if they illustrated the reaction pattern developing in the patient's life. As an illustration, Hill contrasted three statements concerning a male patient. First, "The patient had two years of college." Second, "In his second year in college, the patient was expelled for fighting college policies." Third, "The patient was glad to be expelled in his second year of college for fighting with the dean because it left him free to get a job despite his father's ambitions for him." The first statement told very little about the patient, the second gave one aspect of the patient's character, the third gave a picture of adolescent rebellion.

In preparing for these one-hour conferences, Hill advised that the presentation of the case should not take over 35 or 40 minutes, leaving at least 20 minutes for discussion. He suggested the doctor give an in-

troductory survey of the patient in not over 10 minutes, this to alert the audience to see the problems most troubling to the therapist, and so to keep the discussion on the main topics, then to give brief identifying data in a few sentences. As an example, Hill wrote: ''The patient is a 31-year-old single Catholic plumber who stated, 'They sent me here because they think I am a spy.' ''

A study of patients' folders indicates how thoroughly the plan of care and treatment was developed under Hill: Sally (an assumed name), an unmarried women of 19, was admitted in June 1952, at the earnest request of her mother. There had been considerable tension between Sally and her mother, and the young woman left home to live with another girl with whom she was having an affair. She had three and one-half years of college training and was working as a laboratory technician. She was placed on B-2, a women's admission hall. There 34 pages of nurses' notes, signed by registered nurses, student nurses or attendants, indicated that Sally was pleasant, cooperative, ate well and slept well. She had good body hygiene, and the blood work, ophthalmoscopic and gynecological tests were all normal. She needed no dental attention. The 60 items in her personal and family history told of a broken home, divorced parents, family conflict, and inability of Sally to live with her mother. She was given six psychological tests: Stanford Binet, Wechsler Bellevue, Rorschach, Thematic Apperception, Draw-A-Person, Word Association, and Bender-Gestalt. These showed that Sally was of superior intelligence, with a score of 136 IQ, indicated no gross mental disturbance, and was possessed of good critical thinking. The tests also indicated a typical neurotic conflict, some unresolved conflicts from early childhood, and homosexual tendencies. She possessed exceptional ability to understand social rules, but was immature emotionally, had little fantasy life, and was self-centered. She was diagnosed as having an adolescent adjustment problem without psychosis. Sally entered into ward activities, enjoyed occupational therapy, walked on the lawn and played tennis. Her therapist saw her many times, and in the end she felt that she understood her problem of adjustment to her mother, and ''that there had been a significant change in her attitude.'' Four months after admission Sally felt she could return home and again attend college. She was placed on parole after a staff conference and thirty days later given her final discharge as ''improved.'' A descriptive letter was sent to her family physician. Sally returned to college and six months later married a childhood acquaintance just out of the Service. An appreciative letter came to Sally's therapist thanking him for ''the fine job you did with my daughter.''

As time went on, Hill had great influence on psychiatry in the Baltimore-Washington area. The Baltimore *Sun* wrote of him: ''The whole development of psychiatry and psychoanalytic training in the Baltimore area stems from him... He was a real pioneer in psychoanalytic medicine in the country.'' He was the founder of and a teacher in the Washington-Baltimore Psychoanalytic Institute, consultant to the National Institute of Mental Health, and President of the American Psychoanalytic Association. His book, *Psychotherapeutic Intervention in Schizophrenia,* grew out of his own clinical work at Sheppard Pratt, as well as such papers as ''On Being Rather Than Doing in Psychotherapy.''

It was chiefly through Hill's efforts that Sheppard Pratt retained its certification as a teaching hospital in the period when such standards were constantly becoming more demanding. Recognition of its standing as a teaching institution was shown by the U.S. Public Health Bureau in making grants.

13. The Restless Fifties

AFTER WORLD WAR II was over, admissions steadily climbed to a high point of 297 in 1950, and rose to 340 in 1955, when the daily average census reached 215. Sufficient graduate nurses and physicians were in attendance, assisted by 80 student nurses. Murdock wrote, "We are now more nearly occupying the position of leadership among the group of hospitals that we have traditionally enjoyed in the past." Some of this increase was due to the establishment of a "Continued Treatment Service," under the charge of Dr. Harold Greenberg. The Trustees now approved of taking more long-term patients who required less attention from the medical staff. There were few "free"patients in Sheppard Pratt — not more than one or two at a given time — but a large number paid less than the fixed rate.

Just when things were going smoothly, the Korean War started in June of 1950, presenting the Hospital with problems similar to those faced in the two World Wars. Insecurity and great restlessness prevailed. Doctors were inducted into the Armed Services, while residents from the University of Maryland were no longer available. Graduate nurses left for the war or more profitable positions, and attendants were drained into war industries. For a time there was a reduction in the number of student nurses, and it soon became necessary to close two wards.

Much higher wages were offered by industry than by hospitals. The Veterans Administration put on a drive for help, and the State mental hospitals raised their wages. Attendants who had been at Sheppard Pratt for ten years were receiving $120.00 a month, plus 44ᶜ an hour overtime. In order to assist with recruitment, the Hospital for the first time employed a Personnel Director, Arthur R. Linton, whose work relieved some of the shortages. Murdock suggested that the Hospital should supply and launder uniforms for porters and maids, provide better recreational facilities, improve working conditions, and give a five percent increase in wages. These suggestions were approved, and employees were put on a nine-hour day, but paid overtime for the ninth hour.

Then in a comparatively short period, Sheppard Pratt lost some valuable employees by retirement or death. Marvin Merryman, Administrative Assistant, who had labored so diligently to keep down expenses, retired after 25 years of valuable service. While he was partially incapacitated for some months before retirement, Miss Caroline Tesar ably assisted in the office. Bertha Ham, RN, a graduate of the Hospital Training School, died in 1952, leaving an estate of $11,229 to the Hospital. Essie Watkins, who spent 50 years in the laundry and dietary department, retired at 80; Goldus Hinton, who also spent 50 years at the Hospital, asked at age 78 to remain a bit longer, and his request was granted. Henry W. Koch, engineer for 48 years, died suddenly.

Elizabeth Green, the third social worker on the Hospital staff, retired in 1952. Murdock could not find a replacement until 1956, when Mrs. Eleanor Entorf came to Sheppard Pratt. She was an able social worker and therapist, rendering knowledgeable service to the Hospital until her retirement in 1970. Alma Bering, Chief Dietician for nearly 30 years, retired August 1, 1953. Murdock wrote of her: "Miss Bering has been a very faithful member of our staff and has devoted her untiring efforts to planning, preparing and serving very fine meals to the patients and staff." The Baltimore Sun also made a pleasing comment: "Miss Bering believes that food should do more than merely satisfy hunger. The preparation of food is life itself to her, and it is an art. Food should bring visual pleasure, it should express one's spiritual values; it should have a social function and serve as the common bond bringing one into pleasanter relationship with one's fellow man. No receipt is com-

ABOVE: *A student nurse catches up with the latest in fashion in the library of the Chapman Building.*
LEFT: *Gardening outside the Casino.*

LEFT: *A view of the Casino from the tower of A Building.*
RIGHT: *Using a pedal-operated jigsaw, patients produced furniture in the wood shop of the Occupational Therapy Department.*

plete for Miss Bering until she has added a dash of her own brand of applied psychology (good old-fashioned common sense). Do that and you can influence people's lives for good, she believes. Miss Bering has been doing this for 30 years. In so doing, she has become recognized as a leader in the field of dietetics. And it has been 30 years of fun because she has been able to work there as she pleased. Miss Bering is essentially a dramatist working with food.''

Murdock told the Board that Bering's place ''will be hard to fill.'' It was, indeed. The work of several who came after her was unsuccessful, and he was forced to turn to Hospital Food Management. This corporation agreed to purchase all the food, employ all the servants in the kitchen, pantry, store rooms, and dining rooms, and undertake the entire business of serving food. Although satisfactory, the added cost the first year was $36,830.61.

During the restless period of the 1950's, the Trustees employed two investment firms to give advice and counsel; the efforts of T. Stockton Matthews, Vice President of the Trustees and a senior partner in the firm of Robert Garrett and Sons, was especially valuable. Special attention was given to ''growth stocks'' as long term investments. T. Rowe Price, an investment counselor, wrote, ''You will recall that our purpose in suggesting the holding of growth stocks and purchasing additional ones was to produce over a period of time growth in *income* as well as in principal to offset the increasing expenses of the Hospital operations.'' The Trustees were advised to ''buy these stocks even at a yield below the going current yield on stocks of more mature companies because eventually the yield would be much higher, and the gain in income greater, if more emphasis were placed on future income rather than on current income.'' Investments were made in such companies as Eastman Kodak, International Business Machines

Corporation, Gulf Oil, and the Texas Company. In 1955, 794 shares of stock were sold for $279,985.91 at a net profit of $175,260.84, and a year later additional sales increased the annual income by $8,876.25. Between 1941 and 1954 the Corpus Account grew by $1,157,037.00, all but $266,160.32 of which came from the profitable exchange of stocks and bonds. It is surprising that any surplus at all was left from Hospital operations, since during the ten-year period, 1950-1960 operating expenses at Sheppard Pratt exceeded the income seven out of the ten years. The sum of $98,433.70 was added in those years to the Corpus by gifts and bequests from twelve donors. The largest gift of $54,107.94 was from Charles J. Gibson of West Virginia. The income from investments in bonds, stocks, mortgages, and rentals held by the Trustees increased from $124,564.52 in 1950 to $200,620.96 in 1960. The total assets of the Corporation in 1955 reached $4,235,508.91, so the advantages of having an investment counsel plus one or two bank presidents on the Board was clearly evident.

Two gifts earmarked for specific purposes proved useful. Helen C. Williams left approximately $25,000 to carry on special research work. Interest was allowed to accumulate and, from time to time, used when other funds were not available. When Thorazine was introduced in the early 1950s, $1,000 was taken from the accumulated income to purchase this expensive drug, which was used with remarkable success. Chlorpromazine and reserpine were prescribed from 1954 on, Sheppard Pratt being one of the first hospitals in the country to use both. Murdock wrote that since these drugs became available, the use of seclusion rooms had decreased 75%; breakage, accidents and injuries, both to patients and those inflicted by patients on personnel had shown a corresponding reduction. Sheppard Pratt now suspended the use

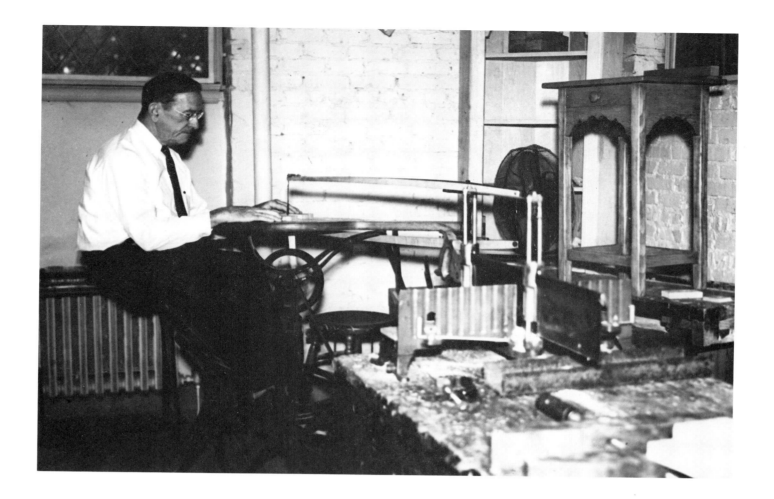

of insulin shock treatment, and reduced electric shock to a minimum.

In 1953 Emma N. Dixon, widow of a former President of the Board, left $1,000 to the Hospital, the interest to be used to purchase food for the many birds on the Hospital grounds. Thus bird houses were built in occupational therapy shops and placed on trees or poles about the grounds. At Christmas time a special occasion was instituted when patients strung popcorn, cranberries, and raisins on long strings which were hung on trees outside their windows.

As each year passed, the Medical Director reported the highest operating budget in the history of Sheppard Pratt. In 1950 it was $921,773.05, three years later it was $1,056,168.42, and in 1957 it had grown to $1,310,189.05.

In 1955 the large implement shed was completely destroyed by fire, with the loss of three tractors, other heavy farm machinery, lumber, and small tools. Insurance covered much of the loss, but replacement of special tools took several years.

Yet for many months the farm and garden showed a loss. Although the dairy was credited with twenty to thirty thousand dollars worth of milk used each year in the kitchens and dining room, and a large amount for chickens, eggs, pork and beef raised on the place, the cost of labor, feed, and fertilizer caused an annual loss of from five to ten thousand dollars. As the city pushed nearer and nearer to the Hospital, keeping men to milk the cows and harvest the crops became increasingly difficult, so it was decided to replace the cows with steers. On November 2, 1955, a well-advertised auction was held on the grounds and the herd of 84 head was sold for $18,436.98. Grazing of steers in the fields saved the expense of mowing, and soon the patients were accustomed to watching shorthorn beef cattle feeding in the fields.

In June of 1955, the Medical Director reported to the Trustees, "the past four months have been one of the most unsettling periods in the Hospital." He added, "There was unrest among the employees over the employment of one colored woman, which was not anticipated." More serious was a wave of suicides that occurred and received much publicity. After nearly six years without a suicide, two came close together in 1955, and the next year there were five. All the latter occurred away from the Hospital among patients on parole who seemed to be much improved and soon ready to be discharged. All five had problems to face when they left the sheltering walls of Sheppard Pratt, and apparently they were unable to handle them.

Now patients in the Hospital were more carefully studied, and those who seemed especially upset were moved to more protected locations. "The process," Murdock added, "was no answer to the problem and sometimes did more harm than good, creating a feeling of frustration." A contagious hysteria among other patients often followed a suicide of one of their number. Of prime importance was that the staff should prevent the patients being confronted by stresses they could not endure, and help them build inner forces strong enough to enable them to meet certain types of reality stresses.

During this decade, Dr. Hill's book, *Psychotherapeutic Intervention in Schizophrenia*, received a good deal of attention and was highly praised. The question of members of the professional staff seeing private patients arose, and formal regulations were written to cover such practice. Senior physicians were permitted to see private patients outside the Hospital hours with the understanding that this would not conflict with their primary responsibilities to Sheppard Pratt. If they saw private patients on Hospital time, for some very special reason, it was by special arrangement and the fees were paid to Sheppard Pratt. Mem-

bers of the intermediate staff could see private patients outside of Hospital hours only with the specific permission of the Medical Director, and residents could not follow such a practice at all.

The usual shortage of attendants was filled by a superior group of men and women driven out of Europe because of the anti-Communist uprising in Hungary. Those who were deficient in English were given special instruction; and, for many, clothing was supplied by the American Friends Service Committee. As late as 1958, Murdock wrote of this group: "We have few attendant problems due to the Hungarians. Almost all have stayed, and they are an intelligent, cheerful, competent group of young people. They recognize we have done a great deal for them, thus their attitude toward the Hospital is outstandingly good."

In the mid-fifties, Murdock was disturbed by the constant fluctuation in the patient census. "There is no complete explanation for this comparatively sudden change in the picture." But there was a general change in the psychiatric situation. While once there was no psychiatric treatment center between Atlanta and Baltimore, now there were several. Many hospitals, including the University of Maryland, added psychiatric units. New forms of treatment — insulin, electric shock, the use of carbon dioxide — and the newer drugs enabled patients to return home much earlier. Some remained in the Hospital for only a brief period returning home on medication.

Because of natural deaths among the long-term patients at the Hospital, and the lack of ability to continue paying the rising costs, the Continued Treatment Service had declined in numbers. Families now seemed willing to send the older members to a hospital for treatment and, if no improvement were evident in a few weeks, on to a State hospital. The Veterans Hospital also took many who previously had come to the private hospitals. These general conditions all affected the rate of admissions.

At the same time, there was also strong competition for professional personnel, notably resident physicians, graduate nurses, psychiatric social workers, occupational therapists, and student nurses. In former times, on completing three years residency, many physicians stayed on for several additional years; now these doctors entered private practice or accepted advanced positions in public institutions.

On the brighter side, in December of 1955 Sheppard Pratt learned that it would share in the largest single philanthropic gift in history. The Ford Foundation announced that it would give grants to the privately supported schools and hospitals amounting to five hundred million dollars. The Foundation wished to encourage local responsibility in developing hospital services that would best serve the residents of each community. The Foundation said the grants could be used to improve present facilities, increase training programs, or enlarge research. Forty-six Maryland hospitals were included in the grants, Sheppard Pratt's gift amounting to $119,200.

Of course many suggestions were made for spending Sheppard Pratt's share. Many small much-needed repairs and replacements could absorb the entire amount, but the greatest need seemed to be for a large recreational facility. This would serve for athletic games, for the showing of films and slides, for dances and other social activities, and as an auditorium. Originally, it was thought the new building would include a place for worship, but several Trustees felt that "a deeper religious feeling and more serious contemplation of spiritual things (could) be obtained by persons assembling in a room on Sunday morning that (had) not been used the evening before for moving pictures, a dance, or a basketball game." There was a general feeling that cognizance should be taken of

the religious heritage of the Founder.

Murdock worked closely with Henry Hopkins, the architect. The new building (now called the Ford Building) centered about a large, high-ceilinged room, 65 feet long, and 46½ feet wide. The floor was unobstructed, the walls were paneled and suitable for all purposes. Locker and rest rooms were below, plus dressing rooms for stage productions and concerts, a fireproof room for motion picture projectors, several offices, smaller rooms for games, and a kitchen. The low bid, by John K. Ruff, Inc., was $263,350, which required the Trustees to supplement considerably the amount donated to the Hospital by the Ford Foundation.

A small Meeting House constructed adjacent to the recreation building and connected to it by a covered arcade, was delightful. Built of brick, it was a copy of an ancient Quaker structure. Inside, a facing platform corresponding to the area used in the past by Quaker ministers, and the three rows of benches were all in good taste. Highback chairs faced a large fireplace. On the exterior was a plaque inscribed:

FRIENDS MEETING HOUSE
ERECTED TO THE MEMORY OF
MOSES SHEPPARD
A MEMBER OF THE RELIGIOUS SOCIETY OF FRIENDS
AND TO MEMORIALIZE AND PERPETUATE THE
OBSERVANCE OF FRIENDLY PRINCIPLES WHICH HAVE
INSPIRED AND GUIDED THIS INSTITUTION FOR
OVER ONE HUNDRED YEARS
1853-1958

ABOVE LEFT: *Windy Brae was the residence of the Medical Superintendent before increased housing for nurses and young physicians was needed.*
ABOVE: *The two brick wings of Windy Brae held rooms for approximately 80 nurses. The old portion of the house provided apartments for junior physicians, kitchen and dining facilities, a library, and a lecture room.*
BELOW: *X-Ray technician Edward N. Phillips in the radiology department, housed in the Reception Building.*

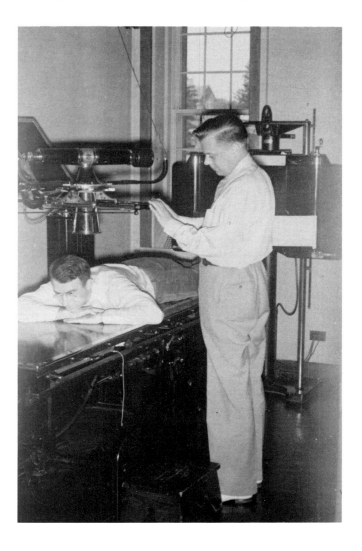

14. Strengthening the Staff

IN THE 1950's the quality of care and treatment of patients severely declined in most State institutions, which were both overcrowded and understaffed. For obvious reasons professional writers sometimes referred to these hospitals as "snake pits." Medical schools were graduating more well-trained psychiatrists schooled in new methods, especially the use of the recently perfected medications, but the demands for psychiatric care expanded to such an extent that young psychiatrists who usually remained at a teaching institution for several years after the training period now went directly into private practice. In the hospitals, this brought about staff shortages, and eventually many foreign-born and foreign-trained physicians were accepted. In 1959, there were 13,000 openings for approved internships in American hospitals while only 7,000 graduates of American medical schools were available to fill them! In that year, serving on hospital house staffs there were 12,000 graduates of foreign medical schools from 91 countries, recruited chiefly from the Philippines, Mexico, Turkey, Korea, Greece, Japan and India. Their language problems and their differing cultural backgrounds proved to be a distinct handicap in the field of psychiatry. At Sheppard Pratt, Dr. Murdock appointed a few graduates from foreign medical schools, but never in large numbers.

Representatives of the accrediting agencies said that the accreditation of Sheppard Pratt might be in jeopardy if the numbers of foreign physicians were increased. It was also suggested that more mature physicians be added to the staff, and steps were taken to cut down the amount of time the residents spent away from the Hospital. In the early fifties, residents spent thirteen hours a week elsewhere, enlarging their experience, especially in the observation of the care and treatment of children. Some questioned whether sufficient experience could be provided for young doctors away from a university setting.

The diagnostic clinic held at the Hospital ended because of lack of patronage, but in 1958 Murdock budgeted $18,000 to set up a model Child Guidance Clinic. He reported to the Governor, "The Child Guidance Clinic is in operation. The supervising people are very competent and are screening patients very carefully. Our resident physicians are very enthusiastic about the possibilities of participating in this project."

Usually two to ten adolescent inpatients were at Sheppard Pratt, admitted for the same reasons that adult patients sought the Hospital, "for supportive reeducational or analytic psychotherapy." It was suggested that this number be enlarged, but Murdock said that "he would need to take a long look before establishing special facilities for adolescents. He questioned whether a psychiatric hospital was indeed the best place for younger patients. He added: "We do take court-involved delinquents when it looks as though the request for hospitalization is not simply to evade facing up to their responsibilities...we have no objections to long-term residential youngsters. We do take overtly psychotic youngsters. Adolescents are absorbed in occupational and recreational therapy. We consider academic teaching secondary in importance. When indicated, arrangements are made on an individual basis, either in nearby schools or by tutor."

Earlier, to meet one of the suggestions made by the accrediting board, Murdock suggested that the costly residential program be abandoned, and in its place experienced physicians be employed who would give at least half-time to the Hospital. He would hand over the training of psychiatric residents to the large medical schools. He felt that "the whole present intern-residency system has an element of

BELOW: *As the city pushed nearer and nearer the Hospital, keeping men to milk the cows and harvest the crops became increasingly difficult. It was decided to replace the cows with steers. The herd of 84 dairy cows was sold in 1955 for $18,436.98 at an auction held on Hospital grounds.*

ABOVE: *Hospital staff members join together to simulate a group therapy session. Everyone in the picture seems to be enjoying a cigarette — a sign of the times which one would not likely see today.*

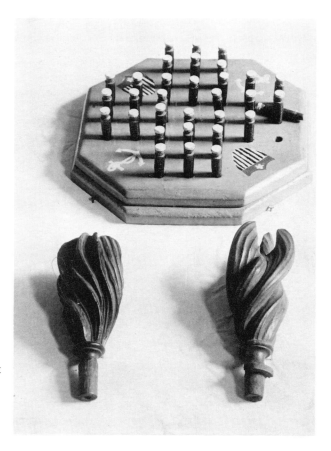

RIGHT: *A peg board and flames for a high boy or clock top, made by an Occupational Therapy aide.*
FAR RIGHT: *A display of crafts produced in Occupational Therapy sessions.*

exploitation which is rapidly becoming outmoded.'' If this substitution were made, the physical needs of patients, then so well cared for by Dr. Newland E. Day, Personnel Physician and Medical Advisor, would be transferred to local physicians. Many of the staff disagreed with such a plan, and felt that it would cause the work of the Hospital to deteriorate. The US Public Health Service did provide some grants for the training program, but these were small, the total averaging under $5,000 a year.

The only other means by which more mature physicians could be brought to Sheppard Pratt was to create an ''open staff.'' The administrators of the Hospital had always tried to carry out the wishes of Moses Sheppard, and in regard to an open staff, the only directive that might apply was the wish ''that each patient shall have an attendant when it may appear useful.'' This was interpreted to mean that ''general medical and psychiatric care and attention included all psychiatric treatment of every kind; all nursing care and attention; and all medication should be provided as they seem indicated at no additional or separate charge, regardless of the rate the patient paid.'' This practice avoided the possibility ''of anything being done or not done for a patient in terms of what he could pay'' and was one of the reasons why the resources of the patient and his family were considered in establishing the rate.

Murdock was in favor of an open staff plan. He maintained Sheppard Pratt had always had good relations with local physicians because the Hospital made every effort to return the patient after treatment to the referring doctor. The plan would add to the patient's expense, however, since the fee of the visiting physician would be added to the Hospital's charges. The Medical Director recommended that members of a ''visiting staff'' have offices in the Hospital buildings. This would insure regular visits on their part. Visiting staff would be responsible for psychotherapy, and such items as medication, physical treatment and scheduled program would be in the hands of the Hospital staff. It was hoped that such a visiting staff would increase admissions.

Although the Trustees considered that there were ''many unanswered problems'' in connection with the formation of an open staff, agreement was given in principle. The plan was placed in operation, and as of January 1962, the visiting staff consisted of eleven doctors.

The Board of Trustees suffered losses during the 1950s. Herbert M. Taylor, a Trustee since 1941, who was responsible for forming a satisfactory pension plan for employees, died in 1957. T. Stockton Matthews, a Trustee for 28 years, who by his wise counsel had greatly improved the investment policies of Sheppard Pratt, died the following year. Dr. Bliss Forbush, Headmaster of the Baltimore Friends School, active in many Quaker humanitarian concerns, was named to fill one of the vacancies. John E. Motz, President of the Mercantile Safe Deposit and Trust Company, Treasurer of the Stony Run Friends Meeting, who was a leader in Baltimore urban development and other civic concerns, was named to fill the second vacancy.

Mary R. Morrissey, the able librarian who had served Sheppard Pratt for 31 years, retired in 1959. Her place was taken by Eleanor E. H. Carter, a gracious person to whom the patients quickly turned for advice concerning their reading needs. Henrietta G. Price, who developed the Occupational Therapy Training School, retired in 1958. E. D. Davila, an artist, became Acting Director. Margaret E. Newcomb, the dynamic Director of Nurses, retired the same year.

But the unexpected death of Dr. Lewis B. Hill in 1958 was truly a calamity. Murdock wrote that ''he

was truly irreplaceable.'' Not only had he been a great leader and teacher at Sheppard Pratt, but he had exerted a tremendous influence on psychiatry in the entire field. After his death, the local psychoanalytic institute established the Hill Memorial Lecture in his honor. Later, a new greenhouse at the Hospital would carry his name.

Murdock moved at once to find suitable replacements for the vacancies. In filling the position of Director of Nurses, he was fortunate in securing the services of Theresa G. Muller, whose training and experience were exceptional. Author of a number of papers in her field, Muller's book, *Foundations of Human Behavior: Dynamic Psychology in Nursing*, was of real assistance to students who desired a foundation for understanding the psychodynamics of human behavior. Muller began her work at Sheppard Pratt in September of 1959. Her wisdom, organizational ability and great dignity gave a lift to the Nursing Department. While at the Hospital her second book, *Fundamentals of Psychiatric Nursing*, was completed.

One of Muller's first moves was to bring Alice Burton back to the Hospital as Assistant Director of Nurses and Coordinator of Clinical Instruction of student nurses. Burton had first come to Sheppard Pratt in 1949 following some years of teaching in Massachusetts. After graduating from The Johns Hopkins School of Nursing, she entered The Phipps Clinic, where she became a department head. An excellent teacher who exuded enthusiasm and verve, she made an excellent second in command on her return to the Hospital. Muller also found in Mrs. Alice Y. Skipper (whom at least two Directors called a tower of strength) a valuable associate. Intensely loyal to Sheppard Pratt and the nursing profession, Mrs. Skipper demanded that her fellow workers give their best to the Hospital. She was an inspiration to all younger nurses.

In the Department of Psychology, Dr. Shaffer continued the longstanding cooperation between Sheppard Pratt and The Johns Hopkins University Department of Psychology, which had begun in the days of Dr. Dunton and Dr. Saunders. Shaffer was assisted by Dr. Mary D. Ainsworth, Associate Professor at the University, and Mrs. Florence Carson, an Instructor, who brought their students to the Hospital for clinical experience. Meanwhile, Shaffer gathered material for his second book, *Fundamental Concepts in Clinical Psychology*, a very readable book of much value to students in the field.

Dr. Joseph D. Lichtenberg, a graduate of Swarthmore College and The Johns Hopkins University Medical School, came to Sheppard Pratt in 1954 and remained as Clinical Coordinator until mid-1960, after which he frequently returned to serve as a member of the teaching staff.

In 1957, Murdock appointed a physician who had profited by wide experience before coming to America. Dr. Zoltan John Levay was a Hungarian who had trained at the Royal University Medical School. He served in his nation's army until the country was overrun by the Soviets. He was then employed by the United States forces until he had an opportunity to work in Pakistan. Throughout many vicissitudes and colorful experiences, he retained his sense of humor and compassion for others. He was well suited to be the Chief of the Continued Treatment Service, a position he held into 1963.

A second ''foreign doctor'' to make a major contribution to the Hospital was Rolfe B. Finn. A graduate of Aukland University College, he had taken medical training at the University of Otago and further work in England. After serving in two psychiatric hospitals, he gained his Diploma in Psychological Medicine and his analysis under Dr.

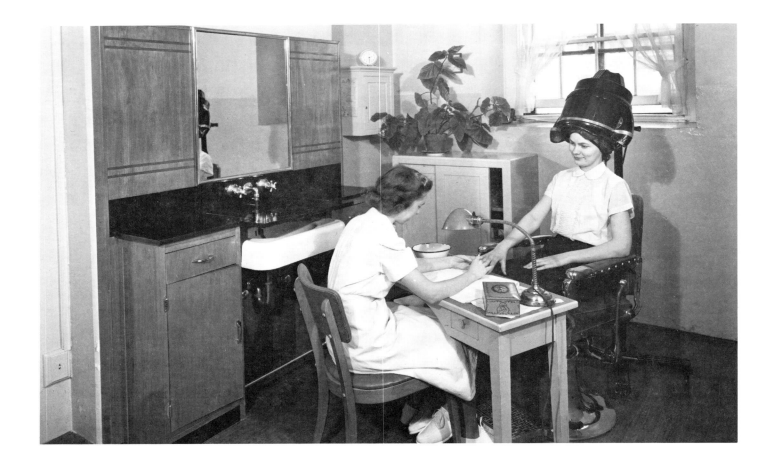

J. A. Hatfield of London. Finn was Chief of Service for one year, 1958-59, and was persuaded to return in 1964 to be Director of Environmental Therapy.

In his efforts to strengthen the staff of Sheppard Pratt, Murdock achieved an outstanding success in 1959 in bringing to the Hospital a distinguished, nationally known figure. Previously he had written Dr. Robert T. Morse in Washington, DC: ''We are thinking in terms of a well-rounded, mature individual, analytically oriented, who has a wide enough familiarity with psychiatric thinking to be able to extract the good parts from a wide variety of psychiatric schools and concepts and meld them into a constructive experience for each patient. Such a person would operate here by example and precept, so that the residents and junior physicians would have a model and a mentor to whom they would turn for guidance, advice and instruction.'' These hopes were all fulfilled when Lawrence S. Kubie, MD, ''psychoanalyst, writer, teacher, and polemicist,'' joined the staff in 1959.

Kubie took his AB at Harvard University, completed graduate work at Columbia University, and received medical training at The Johns Hopkins University School of Medicine. After serving as Instructor-in-Charge of the neuroanatomical clinic under Dr. Adolf Meyer, he studied neuropathological techniques in various European clinics. He then entered a period of association with Drs. Flexner and Sabin in the Rockefeller Institute for Medical Research. Under a National Research Fellowship, Kubie worked from 1928 to 1930 in clinical neurology and neuropathology at the National Hospital for Nervous Diseases in London, where he took his analysis with Edward G. Glover, then Scientific Director of the British Institute of Psychoanalysis. Launched on his analytic practice and teaching, Kubie was associated for the next 25 years with the New York Neurological Institute, the New York Psychoanalytic Institute, Mt. Sinai Hospital, Yale University (where he was Clinical Professor of Psychiatry), and Columbia University. After coming to Sheppard Pratt, he was appointed to the faculty of the Baltimore Psychoanalytic Institute, became Clinical Professor of Psychiatry at the University of Maryland and lecturer at his alma mater, The Johns Hopkins Medical School.

Kubie's influence was valuable and far-reaching at the Hospital, where his teaching stimulated the senior staff as well as the residents. He also lectured and taught Baltimore groups, and spoke before national conventions. After five years as Director of Training, he lightened his load in 1963, although each resident still had the opportunity to present cases for his evaluation. In his evaluations, the one-way vision observation room served as a useful adjunct. In 1970, Kubie became Senior Associate in Research and Training.

Kubie enjoyed thinking of himself as a ''gadfly,'' which he was! He attacked many theories held by psychiatrists, and urged reforms both in training of psychiatrists and in treatment of patients. He did not think the young resident should be treating psychotic patients, but instead should begin his training in the pediatric ward and work with adolescents and young adults. In doing this, he could observe the neurotic process through various moments of stress. Kubie thought many of the current avenues along which psychiatry was moving were blind alleys. He thought most community-psychiatric programs, which featured short-term treatment of a large number of people in local situations, did little permanent good. Many individuals, he felt, needed to be removed from family, friends, and their jobs, and should be placed for a time in a pleasant, cloistered setting far removed from the tur-

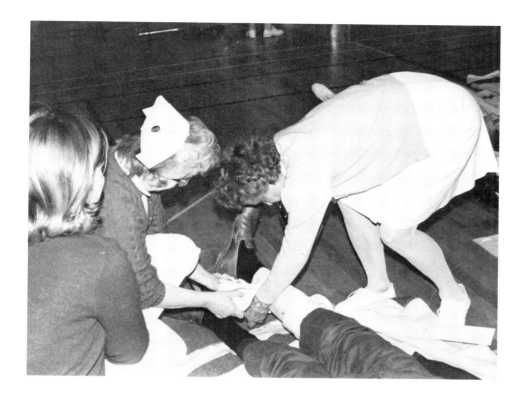

moils of life. He regretted that many patients in public hospitals were stuffed with drugs and sent home without anyone's having discovered the cause of their disorder.

Kubie's most heretical suggestion, advanced as early as 1946, was enlarged on, attacked, rebutted, and reinforced over the next 20 years. His controversial suggestion directed that a new discipline in medicine should be established, leading to the degree of Doctor of Psychological Medicine or Doctor of Psychotherapy. The foundation of this new discipline would be the basic study of human biology and the organismic approach, followed by work in the behavioral sciences, clinical psychology, social pathology, sociology, and cultural anthropology, with strong emphasis on psychopathology, normal and abnormal human development.

Statistics and research methods should be included, Kubie maintained, to improve scientific thinking, in addition to all forms of psychotherapeutic methods, possibly including psychoanalysis. A storm of protest instantly arose when Kubie declared it was not necessary for the individual educated in this new discipline to hold an MD degree. This, to all those working in the field of psychotherapy and psychoanalysis, was rank heresy. But as Dr. Leo H. Bartemeier once wrote, "He (Kubie) can see more clearly than others whatever needs clarifying, correcting and improving. His criticisms are always constructive and he never lacks the courage to present them." He was always guided, however, as Edward Glover once said, "by compulsive benevolence."

Another of the more important men Murdock brought into the Hospital family was Dr. Robert W. Gibson. He joined the staff in 1960 as Clinical Director. Gibson came with a rich background of experience; he was to add new ideas and new life to Sheppard Pratt, exercising greater and greater influ-

ence as the months passed, in an ever-widening circle. A graduate of the University of Pennsylvania Medical School, he had interned at Bryn Mawr Hospital and the New Jersey State Hospital, and had continued his psychiatric training at the VA Hospital at Coatesville, Pennsylvania, and the University of Pennsylvania Hospital. During the Korean War, Gibson was assigned to the Army Hospital at Camp Pickett in Virginia and the US Naval Hospital in Bethesda, Maryland. Gibson became clinical administrator at Chestnut Lodge and research psychiatrist at Chestnut Lodge Research Institute. His psychoanalytic training was taken in the Washington Psychoanalytic Institute, in which he became an instructor and later a Supervising and Training Analyst. His published papers covered research in regression; the manic depressive patient; introjection, identification and identity formation; schizophrenia; and more general subjects such as "The Psychiatric Consultant and the Juvenile Court," "The Family Background and Early Life Experience of the Manic-Depressive Patient," "Patient-Staff Relationships Change with Environment," "Family Background and Interpersonal Dynamics of Depressed Patients," "Contribution of Psychoanalysis to Psychotherapy with Psychotic Patients," and "Patient Work Programs in the Private Psychiatric Hospital."

As Clinical Director at Sheppard Pratt, Gibson was in charge "of what happens to patients, to see that the patient's experience was constructive, internally, interpersonally and socially." He did the programing and scheduling of the activities of the junior, assistant, and resident physicians. He explored sources of information about advances and changes in the scientific and medical fields, passing his findings on to the staff. He evaluated the use of new drugs, safeguarding their use.

15. Major Decisions

IN THE EARLY DAYS of the 1960's many changes came to Sheppard Pratt that vitally affected the future of the Institution. There were three losses on the seven-man Board of Trustees. From the time of his appointment in 1930, J. Kemp Bartlett, Jr., always took a keen interest in the welfare of the Hospital. Named President in 1941, he was active until his death in 1961. Hooper S. Miles, who was a member of the Board for 20 years, resigned in 1963. Chairman of the Board of the Maryland National Bank, he was also Treasurer of the State of Maryland. In the same year, the Trustees lost by death a second valuable 20-year member. Philip E. Lamb made a unique contribution to the Hospital. He was a real estate developer, and served as Chairman of the Educational Committee in charge of the Baltimore Friends School. As head of the Farm and Grounds Committee, Philip Lamb visited the Hospital each week. Responsible for seeing that the grounds were kept in beautiful condition, he saw that new trees and shrubs were planted regularly.

Dr. Bliss Forbush succeeded J. Kemp Bartlett as the ninth President of the Trustees and, with his wife, soon moved into Fordham Cottage. He became well acquainted with the management of the Hospital and with the care and treatment of patients through regular visits to all departments. John A. Luetke-meyer, who succeeded Hooper Miles as Treasurer of the State, gave a great amount of time to the activities of the Board. His assistance in dealing with the many financial transactions which came in this period was invaluable. W. Berkeley Mann, an engineer, who was President of Wolfe and Mann Manufacturing Company, brought an important and unique point of view to the Trustees, as did Norris W. Matthews, a retired chemist. Judge Reuben Oppenheimer was appointed to the Board in 1963. A graduate of the Harvard Law School, he became a member of the Supreme Bench in 1955 and of the Maryland Court of Appeals in 1964. As Chairman of the State Board of Correction from 1947 to 1961, he was instrumental in establishing the Patuxent Institute for treatment of mentally and emotionally defective prisoners.

Dr. John T. King completed 30 years of dedicated service to the Board on September 27, 1963. He had been a member of the Hospital Executive Committee and served as Chairman of the Nurses Training Committee. Board members enjoyed his fellowship and gratefully accepted his sagacious counsel.

In 1963, for greater convenience and to save rent, the downtown office of the Trustees was moved to the ground floor of the Chapman Building. At this time, Mr. Alfred W. Strahan retired as Secretary and manager of the office, following 60 years of service. Mr. Strahan came to the Board in 1902, and remembered when the records were kept in big old-fashioned ledgers, often propped up on high Dickensian desks. He described his association with the Trustees "as an education in itself." Strahan was also an able artist and an ardent gardener.

Under Strahan, the Finance Department achieved a remarkable record of collections. In the five-year period 1957-1961, with $7,105,798.97 received from board and medical fees, only $18,074.81 was not collected, an average of only .0025%. As the accounting system was quite inadequate for the growing needs of Sheppard Pratt, the auditing firm of Main, Lafrentz & Co. was employed to study and prepare recommendations for a new system. In 1964 they recommended that an accrual system be established that would control costs, provide a basis for planning, and assist in the assessment and evaluation of departmental operations. This was placed in the charge of the new Secretary and Comptroller, Frederic F. Hinze. Hinze came to Sheppard Pratt to

LEFT: *Social workers provide support in many different ways — at times no words are necessary.*
BELOW: *Bliss Forbush enjoys a reception by the swimming pool.*

do his alternate army service. A graduate of the Wharton School, he had had experience in a large accounting firm. Hinze was an alert young man, and was assisted and advised by Caroline Tessar, Secretary and Assistant Comptroller.

Some of the Trustees' land had already been taken by the State, and a new major county road through the northern portion of their property was projected. Since it was already proved that keeping cows and raising steers in the pasture land was unprofitable, the Trustees were not averse to selling land not needed for hospital operations. They were besieged by developers who wished to purchase part of the property for a variety of purposes — two churches, a nursing home, and a doctors' office building. The Trustees, however, preferred to have the land go to the College; they could envisage future cooperation between Sheppard Pratt, the College, and the two neighboring hospitals in nursing education, training of health workers, social workers, and students of normal and abnormal psychology. Dr. Murdock was confident that satisfactory relationships could be worked out with the Greater Baltimore Medical Center and St. Joseph's Hospital. He thought each hospital eventually would have a psychiatric unit, supplied with psychiatric consultants from Sheppard Pratt. "Our residents now go down to Hopkins and the University of Maryland," he wrote, "but now presumably they would work in the outpatient department of our two neighboring hospitals and in their Children's Clinics."

In 1961 began what appears in the records as "The Financial Crisis." In the past, with few exceptions, the Trustees were able to set aside the income from their investments for future building operations. The total plant had been secured in this manner, some $280,000.00 of Trustees' income being used to complete the most recently constructed Ford Building

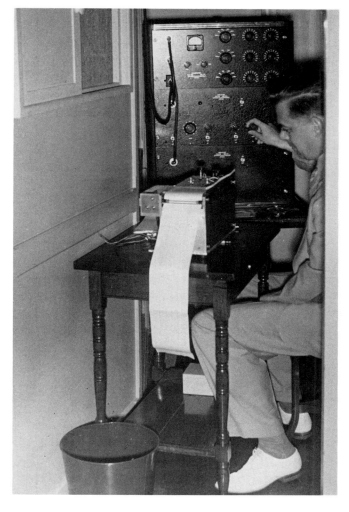

ABOVE: *A technician operates the electroencephalograph recorder.*

and Meeting House. It was expected that the operating costs of the Hospital would be covered each year by the income from patients' board and medical fees. The situation began to change in the mid-fifties and became more marked by 1960. By 1964, the weekly loss per patient had risen to $13.64, and with these rising losses it became necessary to draw on the income from the investments as follows:

1960.................$100,507.07
1961.................$216,472.83
1962.................$128,611.69
1963.................$300,198.08
1964.................$63,031.95
1965.................$157,343.94

The rapid increase in operating costs, combined with the low admission rate, greatly disturbed Murdock and the members of the Board. Many discussions followed. It was recognized that sudden fluctuations in the census, which came without any perceivable cause, could not be met by salary adjustments, which accounted for over 70 % of the budget. Doctors and nurses were employed many months in advance. It took a long time to build up a smooth and efficiently operating organization that used so many diversified talents. The Medical Director did not feel that the budget could be cut, for salaries and wages were already too low, and in view of the age of the buildings, repairs and renovations ran to a high figure.

The only place where money could be saved, Murdock thought, was by giving up the Residency Training Program, which cost approximately $100,000 a year. If this were done, he would replace the younger men by senior psychiatrists who would give most or all of their time to the Hospital. There was a possibility, he admitted, that the atmosphere at the Hospital would change if it were no longer a major teaching institution, but this need not happen

if the house doctors were carefully chosen. On the other hand, Kubie warned that if the training program were abandoned, the Hospital might lose its accreditation; and to employ only senior psychiatrists would be as costly as the training program.

To fill the financial need, both Kubie and Murdock suggested that the Trustees undertake a fund-raising campaign, but those whom they consulted advised against it. It was said that mental hospitals found it very difficult to secure men and women who would personally solicit individuals, which was the heart of any campaign. This was because of the so-called stigma attached to mental institutions. It was not considered wise to ask former patients or their families for money, so that, unlike the alumni of schools and colleges, those who once used the hospital could not be counted on to contribute to its development. Thus, no effort at Sheppard Pratt was yet made to campaign for outside money.

Murdock was much influenced by an article by J. Martin Myers, MD, Executive Medical Officer of the Psychiatric Institute of the Pennsylvania Hospital. Dr. Myers took a gloomy look at the future of private psychiatric hospitals. He noted the many opportunities now existing for the care of the mentally ill, the increased cost of private hospitals, and the limited aid given by the various insurance plans. In 1961 Blue Cross paid for a very limited number of days of hospitalization; commercial companies were less discriminatory, but many major medical policies written for $10,000 maximum were reduced to $1,500 for mental cases. Some commercial policies contained a clause, "mental or nervous disorder benefits will be paid only for expenses when confined to a hospital which does *not* specialize in the treatment of mental diseases." Myers, whose paper was circulated among the Board members, ended his paper with the statement that "because of the

OPPOSITE: *Group therapy as interpreted by artist Aaron Sopher.*
ABOVE: *The towers of the A and B Buildings have always served as symbols of the Hospital.*
LEFT: *Sopher captures the fear of being left alone in the world, a feeling experienced by many elderly patients.*

wide variety of types of psychiatric treatment available (private practice, units in general hospitals, use of drugs, increase in home care) isolated psychiatric hospitals are doomed to go the way of debtors' prison.''

With Myers' article in mind, Murdock suggested to the Trustees six possible courses of action:

1. To sit tight and make no major changes, to wait to see if the organization of the open staff (recently approved) would increase the patient population.
2. To increase the capital funds by attracting donors; or to sell 200 to 225 acres of land, not needed for the operation of the Hospital, thus improving the annual income by as much as $100,000.
3. To sell all the land and buildings, and with the funds secured construct a 50 to 60 bed hospital on the Auburn property, which was originally purchased for a Children's Center.
4. To sell out and hold the funds while searching for a proper use for them within the intent of the Founder.
5. To pool the resources of the Hospital with other health organizations, existing or to be established.
6. To ''lower our sights, abandon many of our treatment efforts...and become a custodial institution of inferior quality.''

Murdock believed that the sixth possibility outlined was ''unthinkable'' and the fourth and fifth very difficult to achieve, even if wise, without violating the directives of Moses Sheppard. He warmly approved of the first or second option, and leaned in the direction of the third. At times he felt that the best plan to follow would be to make a new start with a small, heavily endowed hospital, primarily devoted to the treatment of a small number of patients.

Dr. King expressed the feeling of his fellow Trustees when he said that ''he would regret to see the Hospital, which could take care of 250 patients, reduced to a hospital to care for 50.'' For the time being, the Board decided to ''sit tight,'' and to continue to negotiate with the State officials for the sale of additional land to be used by Towson State College. Through the time and effort given by the members of the Board, and their Attorney, James D. Peacock, $1,982,310.92 was added to the endowment of the Hospital in 1963 and 1964, making the invested funds total $5,074,298.78.

In 1962 social changes of the outside world also impinged more sharply on Sheppard Pratt with the request for the admission of a Negro patient. The President of the Board took the matter up with Murdock, who expressed himself candidly. ''I suppose my feelings about admitting a Negro to Sheppard Pratt boil down to this,'' he said. ''Would doing so result in a more therapeutic environment, a situation more conducive to the recovery of our patients from their psychiatric disorders? I am a physician. My role is to treat sick people. I am trying to run a good hopital, not primarily to correct social injustice...If I thought that admitting Negroes or doing anything else would result in better patient care, I would be all for it. I do not see that it would.''

After staff discussions, the subject was taken to the Board of Trustees. In this period of rapid integration change in Maryland, a southern state, and especially in an institution that drew such a large number of its clientele from below the Mason-Dixon Line, the Hospital found, as so many schools and colleges in the State did, that it had never faced the new situation, nor ever made a statement on the subject. These institutions had simply persisted in an

ancient pattern without being challenged. The Board considered the matter carefully and minuted the following on May 17, 1962: "As to integration, it was the sense of the Executive Committee that the Trustees, as far as known, never requested that the Hospital be segregated. They desire that as qualified individuals apply for any position, they be employed, and that patients of other races who would otherwise qualify for admission, be admitted." Most of the porters or cleaning men were Negroes, as were many of the maids; in the Dietary Department, the races were about equally represented. In better paid positions, only whites were employed. A real effort was made from this time on to employ Negro nurses, and a few were secured; but in most cases, the Sheppard Pratt salary scale was not sufficient to attract them. Negro patients were admitted as they applied. But before many months, a graduate of the Meharry Medical School of Fiske University, Dr. James R. Ralph, who had an outstanding record, became a resident. Shortly afterwards, two more Negro physicians were added to the Hospital Staff, and dire predictions concerning admission of Negroes never materialized.

Late in 1962 Murdock submitted a plan for using the Chapman Building as a geriatric center. He explained to the Board that there were two types of elderly people who might profit by such an arrangement. He wrote: "The first is basically a 'home' for elderly people who are no longer able to live alone or to bear the full responsibility for their physical maintenance. Ambulatory but generally failing in strength, they are still alert to their surroundings and able to live comfortably with minimal medical support. A home for such people...should also have facilities to care for them during treatment or prolonged confusional states, and for senile and arteriosclerotic mental conditions, and provision for prolonged physical disabilities requiring bed care, so that the residents of such a home could feel secure about being taken care of under the one roof through everything that might happen to them, except during serious acute medical or surgical illnesses." Murdock pointed out that such an institution would combine the facilities of a custodial residence, a nursing home, and a mental hospital. Murdock suggested that the first floor of the Chapman Building be used for well-integrated elderly people, each with a private room, and with all facilities nearby for social living.

To carry forward his new ideas, Murdock asked that he be allowed to spend the majority of his time with the older patients, plus supervising the operation and maintenance of the physical plant and property, as well as advising the Trustees on financial matters and future planning. The Trustees approved of this shift of duties and appointed Murdock as Administrator and as Consultant in Planning and Development. He assumed the direction of the Chapman Building July 1, 1963.

Murdock continued his plans for the geriatric unit, substituting a friendly atmosphere and a feeling of rejuvenation and interest in daily living rarely found among geriatric patients, where apathy usually abounds. In December of 1964 he asked that he be relieved as Administrator and retain only the responsibility and management of the Chapman Building. In May of 1965, he requested a leave of absence — something he had never enjoyed — and asked to return with no further duties other than as Consultant to the Board. This was approved by the Trustees, who were warmly appreciative of all that he had done for Sheppard Pratt in his 35 year association with the Hospital. On his return from an extended trip, his portrait was painted and hung with those of Doctors Brush and Chapman in the A Building.

16. Multiple Expansion

DR. ROBERT W. GIBSON became Medical Director in July 1963, and in 1965 he assumed responsibility for the complete administration of the Hospital. Having served as Clinical Director at Chestnut Lodge and Sheppard Pratt, he was well prepared to accept new administrative tasks. Gibson's point of view was not parochial. Soon after coming to Baltimore he became a member of the faculty of The Johns Hopkins University Medical School and was appointed Psychiatrist (part-time) at The Johns Hopkins Hospital. He also served as a Training and Supervising Analyst at the Washington Psychoanalytic Institute. A consultant to the Maryland Department of Mental Hygiene, before long Gibson became President of the Maryland Psychiatric Society. In an even wider field, he was a Trustee of the National Association of Private Psychiatric Hospitals and served as a member of the Group for the Advancement of Psychiatry and of the Editorial Board of *Psychiatry*.

As Chairman of the Legislative Committee of the NAPPH, and representing the American Psychiatric Association, Gibson made a major contribution to the development of Medicare. The Medicare Bill, as first proposed, "excluded any institution for the care and treatment of...mental defects." The intent had been to exclude patients from all psychiatric institutions. Gibson spoke before the Department of Health, Education and Welfare, and the Senate Finance Committee advocating a broader interpretation. In his testimony, Gibson urged: "Medicare should serve as an example to private insurance programs to handle the mentally ill as they do persons suffering from other illnesses. It can even influence the opinion of the general public about the mentally ill. No longer will they be a group that must be treated differently and denied the benefits given to others."

Before endorsing new moves that would greatly affect the future of Sheppard Pratt, the Trustees asked Drs. Murdock, Kubie and Gibson to submit their ideas concerning the future. The suggestions were almost overwhelming in scope. The doctors agreed that the Hospital would "enter a new era with much in its favor, an excellent physical plant, a location near two major psychiatric centers, a substantial endowment, and a sound reputation."

Gibson stressed the need of a strong staff of competent people with a variety of talents, adequately compensated, who would not treat Sheppard Pratt "as a way-station of their professional career." He suggested that information concerning the Hospital be circulated more broadly, which could be accomplished through wider distribution of the *Information for Physicians* and the circulation of an annual report, which had been discontinued in 1923. He suggested that Department Heads be asked to describe the work of their areas before the Board of Trustees. To reach new audiences he would plan an annual Scientific Day and establish a Mental Health Week at the Hospital, featuring exhibits and speakers describing professional opportunities in the mental health field.

Kubie presented many suggestions. These ranged from steps to protect the administrator from many details, and at the same time "keep him growing." He thought there could be better use of the grounds, the library, and the community. He advocated using the deserted cowbarn for a roller skating or ice rink and the construction of a swimming pool. He suggested that there be less use of TV by patients, which had "a destructive effect on their lives because of the length of time spent in viewing, rather than in association and cooperation with others." He thought halls could be developed into self-governing units. For the Board, Kubie suggested a larger membership, including representatives of many

ABOVE: Dr. Robert Wagner Gibson was named the fourth
Medical Director of The Sheppard and Enoch Pratt
Hospital in July of 1963.

community bodies, i.e., religious, social, economic, racial, and "above all, women." From his wide experience, Kubie gave many suggestions for improving the Residency Training Program, details of which were thoroughly discussed in staff meetings. He favored establishing a School of Social Psychiatry in which courses for clergymen, school teachers, nurses, policemen, parole officers, lawyers and judges, as well as families of patients, would be available. When questioned about the cost of carrying out his many suggestions, Kubie answered with a twinkle in his eye, "It is immoral for a private psychiatric hospital — or any hospital — to operate in the black!"

With a mind full of ideas, and helpful suggestions from Kubie and Murdock, Gibson began his administration. His first task was to continue the upbuilding of the medical staff; his second to meet the organizational needs of Sheppard Pratt.

Dr. Clarence G. Schulz began his work as Director of Psychiatric Services in 1963. Trained at the Washington University of St. Louis, with a wide variety of experiences at St. Elizabeth's Hospital in Washington, DC and 15 years at Chestnut Lodge and the Washington Psychoanalytic Institute, he was a man "who inspired confidence in people who knew him, one whose psychiatric knowledge and training were impeccable."

Under the joint stimulus of Drs. Gibson and Schulz and Mrs. Rose Kilgalen, who became Director of Nurses in 1966, greater autonomy and responsibility were given to individual members of the medical staff in their day-to-day treatment of patients. The position of Chief of Service was abolished; senior staff members made daily rounds; hall administrators played a more important part in relation to patients; and more individual supervision of residents was supplied by staff psychiatrists or outside consultants.

Stimulating papers by prominent medical figures were reprinted and discussed in the bi-weekly Journal Club, to which outside speakers came from time to time. The working relation between hall nurse and the psychiatrist, ably fostered by Kilgalen, became closer and mutually more supportive.

Coupled with the increased autonomy for staff members, patients were gradually given more freedom, with less regimentation and general relaxation of restrictions. Nearly all patients, except those in the geriatric section, went to the dining rooms. It was the exception for an active treatment patient to be served a tray on the hall. The patients enthusiastically endorsed the newly established cafeteria, where they found greater freedom in having their own choice of foods. Social pressure, unconsciously exerted, resulted in better order and a more pleasing atmosphere. Problems concerning conduct and scheduling were discussed in the Patient-Staff Council, which expanded its activities during the 1960's. More patients were permitted to go unescorted to doctor's appointments or hospital activities such as the library and the Ivy Nook; pay phones were placed in corridors and on many halls. Sign-out sheets were placed on halls and more patients were allowed to leave the grounds. Halls were redecorated, mirrors hung in bedrooms, pictures and posters placed on bedroom walls. Progress from restricted to less restricted halls became more rapid.

Between January 1960 and December 1967 there were 2,396 admissions to the Hospital. In this period, patients were admitted at an increasingly younger age. In 1960, the average age of the males was 37, in 1967, it was 34; the average age of females in 1960 was 42, in 1967, it had dropped to 38. This was chiefly due to the increasing number of adolescents entering the Hospital. It is interesting that the average male

OPPOSITE: *Dr. Lawrence Kubie leads a patient review session with a group of psychiatric residents.*
LEFT: *Mrs. Hilarie Greenston, secretary of Mt. Airy School.*
BELOW: *Santa and child discuss Christmas wishes.*

in 1960 was five years younger than the average female, but by 1967 he was *nine* years younger. The proportion of the sexes did not change in these years, remaining at 38.3% males and 61.7% females.

The educational level of those coming to Sheppard Pratt was high: 65% of the men and 47% of the women had attended or graduated from college in 1967; 6% had only an eighth-grade education or less. Housewives represented the largest occupational group, 29.7%, as might be expected from the predominance of women in the Hospital. Professionally or technically trained individuals accounted for 19.3%. Students accounted for another 19.3%. This category had increased from 15% in 1960-63 to 23% in 1964-67. There were also more people admitted who had seen service in the Armed Forces, due to the greater insurance they carried. Patients entering the Hospital through voluntary admissions came to 74%, by certification 19%, and by agreement for treatment of a minor child from 5% in 1960 to 14% in 1967.

The proportion of patients receiving individual psychotherapy rose from 81% in 1962 to 97% in 1966, and was 95% in 1968, "as would be expected in terms of the orientation of the Hospital." The proportion of patients receiving antidepressant drugs did not change, remaining at 8%. Thirty-eight percent received some form of tranquilizers, and 3% were on both an antidepressant and a tranquilizer. The drugs in general use were: chlorpromazine, Sparine, Vesprin, Pacatal, Mellaril, Compazine, Trilafon, Dartal, Stelazine, reserpine. The minor tranquilizers were: Meprobamate, Frenquel, Atarax and Librium. The antidepressants were: Marsilid, Nardil, Dexedrine, Dexamyl, Desoxyn Tofranil, Parnate, Elavil, and Ritalin. Electroshock was little used.

In the 60's insurance entered increasingly into the picture of hospitalization because of steadily rising costs. In the period 1960-1963, 61% of patients entering Sheppard Pratt had some form of insurance; in 1967 the percentage had increased to 80%.

Paralleling the nation's unrest in that decade, the administration of the nursing staff suffered because of rapid change in leadership. Although dedicated service was constantly given to inpatients by the staff, in four years there were five Directors of Nurses. Miss Muller, who made a major contribution during her few years at the Hospital, retired in the fall of 1962; Harriet Hodges, RN, MA, withdrew in 1963; Kathryn S. Bixby served only two years. Stability came again when Rose K. Kilgalen, RN, MS, took charge of the Nursing Department in January 1966. Her abilities were already well known to Gibson and Schulz because of their association together at Chestnut Lodge.

During her term as Director, Bixby had constantly brought to the attention of the Trustee Committee on Nursing the great need for better salaries at all nursing levels. And in March of 1964 new wage scale standards were set that at the time matched the best hospital levels in Baltimore.

These were: attendants at $1.39 to $1.55 an hour, with senior attendants from $1.55 to $1.70; staff nurses at an annual salary of $4,300 to $5,300; staff nurses with BS degree from $4,600 to $5,600; head nurses from $5,300 to $6,500; supervising nurses from $5,500 to $6,500, with a BS from $6,000 to $7,000 and with an MA from $6,500 to $7,500. Excellent patient care could not have been given through recent decades without the assistance of the student nurses. Until late in the 1960's there were six or seven affiliated general hospitals that sent their students to Sheppard Pratt for a 13-week period of psychiatric training.

The cost per student of the student training program, estimated in 1959 to be $362 per student, rose

by 1962 to $424. The role of the student nurse, however, was changed by a new trend in nursing schools. The professional nursing association ruled that students in training *could not be used* to meet functional needs of patients. They could observe patients, relate to them, but not provide nursing care.

The rising cost of the training program had been met in part during the late 1960's by a tuition charge of $200 per student. This was not sufficient because, under the new regulation, it was necessary for the Hospital to employ more attendants and registered nurses to do the work once performed by the students. There was also a drive on the part of the professional organization to replace the training of nurses in general hospitals by courses given in collegiate institutions, either a two-year course in the developing junior or community college, or by a four-year baccalaureate degree.

Several Baltimore institutions asked to send their students to Sheppard Pratt to make clinical observations, accompanied by instructors from each college. Catonsville Community College was the first to be accepted, followed by Essex Community College, Baltimore Community College, and students from the four-year BS course from the University of Maryland. But by 1969, Sinai Hospital was the only general hospital continuing to send its student nurses to Sheppard Pratt.

In 1963, Dr. Harold F. Searles, an internationally recognized authority on the psychotherapy of the schizophrenic patient, joined the staff as a part-time consultant and teacher. In more than a score of scientific papers he had made a fundamental contribution to both theoretical understanding and clinical practice. His many papers were gathered together and published in 1966, and his work greatly stimulated the residents and older staff members.

Associated with the Hospital for many years, Dr.

Kent E. Robinson joined the staff on a full-time basis in 1964. For ten years a practicing psychiatrist, he also held an appointment as Assistant Professor of Psychiatry at the University of Maryland as teacher of psychosomatic medicine, and acted as a liaison with other medical specialties in the University Hospital. He was named President of the Maryland Association of Private Practicing Psychiatrists in 1955, and Chairman of the Psychiatric Section of the Medical and Chirurgical Faculty of the State of Maryland in 1958.

Robinson came to Sheppard Pratt as Director of Outpatient Activities, soon establishing the Outpatient Clinic. This provided an excellent training opportunity for residents. Patients in the clinic were accepted on referral by physicians, by social agencies, from other clinics, and by self-referral.

The older Residency Training program at the Hospital was revised and improved by Dr. Kubie in 1960. He declared: "The program consisted essentially of an opportunity to study and to treat a limited number of patients suffering from a variety of potentially reversible psychiatric disorders." Psychotherapy, a planned program of activities, and a therapeutic milieu all played a part in the treatment. A small group of these mentally ill were assigned to each resident, who was carefully supervised by members of the Hospital's staff or by consulting psychiatrists.

In 1965 residents were assigned, under Robinson's supervision, to the Health Service of Goucher College, Towson State College, and Morgan State College. At first, only one resident and one staff psychiatrist went to each college, but the number was gradually increased. According to the organization and wishes of the college health services, the Sheppard Pratt residents evaluated students, held consultations with faculty members concerning the

emotional problems of their students, and were available also to faculty members.

Soon psychiatric services were provided for the Hospital's neighbor, the Greater Baltimore Medical Center. In 1965 six residents from Sheppard Pratt spent a half day a week at GBMC. These arrangements functioned smoothly, as Dr. Robinson was Chief of Psychiatry at the neighboring hospital. In 1966, Dr. Irvin H. Cohen, under a grant from NIMH, became Director of Psychiatric Education at GBMC, providing training for the staff in the psychological aspects of clinical practice in their own specialties.

Dr. Samuel Novey had maintained a long connection with Sheppard Pratt. He was well known in the field of psychiatry through his many papers published in British and American journals. For 14 years he was court psychiatrist to the Baltimore County Circuit Court. Also, he was an Associate Professor of Psychiatry at The Johns Hopkins Medical School. Novey came to the Hospital in 1966 as Director of Training, but he did not have time to carry out his ideas because of his sudden death a few months later.

Novey was followed by Dr. Irvin H. Cohen, a graduate of Johns Hopkins and the University of Maryland, who had filled several administrative positions in psychiatry, among which were Director of Psychiatric Education at Spring Grove State Hospital, teaching and supervision at both Hopkins and Sheppard Pratt. He was Assistant Professor of Psychiatry at Sinai Hospital in Baltimore, and Director of Psychiatric Education at GBMC. Cohen further developed the Residency Training Program, based on the certainty that an understanding of the troubled person was basic, secured through a close person-to-person relationship. Outpatient work, group therapy, family therapy, child psychiatry, clinical administration, consultative psychiatry,

neurology and other specialized learning opportunities were included as part-time assignments throughout the three years of training.

The number of physicians in the training program steadily expanded, made possible by increasing grants from the NIMH. There were ten residents in 1963, 13 in 1964, and 18 in 1965. Included were four General Practitioner Grants, open to physicians who had been in private practice for at least five years in specialties other than psychiatry. In 1966 there were ten first-year residents, and seven each in the second and third years.

As the number of residents increased, it was necessary to enlarge the number of senior psychiatrists, all of whom were engaged in supervision and teaching. Dr. William T. Dixon, who served on the Sheppard Pratt staff for many years, was appointed in 1966 as Senior Psychiatrist. A graduate of Princeton University and The Johns Hopkins Medical School, he secured further training at Payne Whitney Clinic of the New York Hospital, and as an Instructor in Psychiatry at Cornell Medical School. He added great strength to the Hospital staff. Dr. Mariano Veiga, who joined the staff in 1966, spent most of his time teaching residents to work with children and adolescents. Dr. Irving Ryckoff, who collaborated in pioneer family studies conducted at the National Institute of Mental Health, took over direction of Family Therapy, and Dr. Theodore M. Feldberg shared his expertise in Group Therapy. Dr. Thomas J. Preziosi, of the Johns Hopkins faculty, gave a foundation course in neurology each year.

With such an expanding staff, it was necessary to establish a communication center where the work of the residents would be coordinated. This task was given to Miss Louise King, who knew Sheppard Pratt through her 30 years' association. She was appointed Administrative Coordinator.

17. Continuing Progress in the Sixties

THE SEVENTY-FIFTH Anniversary of the opening of Sheppard Pratt was celebrated on June 17 and 18, 1966, by staff members past and present who delivered formal papers before a distinguished group of psychiatrists. Two of the papers, "Moses Sheppard's Interest in Mental Illness," by Bliss Forbush, LL D, and "The Future of the Private Psychiatric Hospital," by Lawrence S. Kubie, MD, ScD, were published as a booklet; all the papers with the remarks of the discussants appeared in book form in *Crosscurrents in Psychiatry and Psychoanalysis*, edited by Dr. Robert W. Gibson. The arrangements for this anniversary followed the pattern of the successful annual Scientific Day Programs, which began in 1964.

In the sixties patient care was enriched through the expansion of the role of the social workers. The Social Service Department functioned as an ancillary service to the therapeutic treatment and was available to families. Referrals dealt primarily with complex family problems, marital difficulties, child-parent relationships, and posthospital planning. With an increase in the adolescent population, it became necessary for the social workers to spend more time with parents.

In the spring of 1965 Mrs. Helen T. Kingsbury joined the Social Service Department and shortly thereafter became Director. As new programs developed and additional social workers were needed, the department played a larger and larger part in the activities of the Hospital.

In line with Sheppard Pratt's long history as a teaching institution, it seemed appropriate to provide a training program for psychiatric social workers. Beginning in 1967 with four graduate students from the West Virginia University Division of Social Work, this program was followed by an affiliation with the University of Maryland, which placed students in both the adult and children's psychiatric areas. In the sixties, social workers participated in the admission of all patients, covered Medicare cases, and were attached as members of the clinical team to each clinical service.

In 1966, Dr. G. Wilson Shaffer became Senior Associate and Consultant in Psychology, and Dr. Gerald A. Whitmarsh became Director of Psychology. A graduate of Trinity College in Hartford, Connecticut, Whitmarsh came to Sheppard Pratt from the Maryland Children's Center, where he had served as Director of Research and Chief of Psychological Services. He was assisted by Phoebus N. Tongas, PhD, a graduate of the University of Toronto and of the Menninger School of Psychiatry. At this time the department was primarily occupied with diagnostic evaluations, giving approximately 450 to 650 tests a year to nearly 200 patients.

The department carried on several teaching functions, often on an informal day-to-day basis, as it assisted the physicians in applying the basic principles of human behavior to specific problems. There were formal lectures and seminars for residents and demonstrations of the Wechsler Adult Intelligent Scale, Rorschach and Thematic Apperception Tests.

In 1968, Whitmarsh became Director of a newly established Department of Research, while Dr. Benjamin Pope took over the leadership of Psychology Services. Dr. Donald H. Saidel transferred to Child Psychiatry where he became Chief Psychologist. Pope, a graduate of the University of Manitoba, took his PhD at the University of California. He came to Sheppard Pratt from the University of Maryland, where he was Professor of Medical Psychology and Director of Psychological Sciences in the Psychiatric Institute. Saidel was a graduate of the University of Rochester, held a Fulbright Exchange Fellowship, and was trained at Menninger's.

TOP: *The Board of Trustees in 1967. Left to right seated: Vice President John A. Luetkemeyer, President Bliss For-bush, and John T. King MD. Left to right standing: Reuben Oppenheimer, Norris W. Matthews, John Motz, W. Berkeley Mann, and Medical Director Robert W. Gibson.*
ABOVE: *The seventy-fifth anniversary of the opening of Sheppard Pratt was celebrated on June 17 and 18, 1966, by staff members past and present who delivered formal papers before a distinguished audience.*

The Department of Research was occupied the first year in developing a system of collecting data on patients and storing it in such a fashion that it could be immediately available. The staff then followed through on items of basic research as well as operational evaluations of hospital programs. In rapid succession there came from this Department five valuable studies:

Research Study 1, *Patient Characteristics at The Sheppard and Enoch Pratt Hospital, 1960-1970.*

Research Study 2, *A Study of Older Patients Admitted to The Sheppard and Enoch Pratt Hospital, 1966-1968.*

Research Study 3, *A Study of Selected Characteristics and Follow-Up Data from The Sheppard and Enoch Pratt Hospital Child Guidance Clinic, 1959-1966.*

Research Study 4, *An Analysis of Some Patient Characteristics Associated with the Use of Psychotropic Drugs at Sheppard Pratt.*

Research Study 5, *Follow-Up Survey of Admissions, 1960-1964, The Sheppard and Enoch Pratt Hospital.*

Research Study 2 was of special interest because it covered older patients admitted to Sheppard Pratt under Medicare between July, 1966, and July, 1968. There were 62 patients in this category, 22.6% male and 77.4% female. The mean age of the males was 73 and of the females 71. The majority came from Maryland, with 24% from other states. Of this number, 81% had retired, 45% were widowed, 8% divorced and 33% married at the time of admission. Coming directly from their homes were 64%, from other hospitals 19%. The greatest precipitating cause of hospitalization was a death in the family, the next highest was physical illness, and the third greatest was retirement. The most common symptom shown was depression (by 71%), the next anxiety (by 59%), the third confusion (56%), and the fourth memory impairment (by 35%.) Suicidal intent affected 30%, and insomnia, 27%. Of those admitted, 90% received occupational therapy, 80% had individual psychotherapy, and 62% received chemotherapy. On leaving the Hospital, 66% were considered improved, 34% were not. On discharge, 22% entered nursing homes, 20% continued to live alone at home, 18% were returned to a spouse, and another 18% to other relatives. In an address quoted in the *Towson Times,* Gibson said these figures demonstrate "that substantial numbers of older patients are being fully rehabilitated and achieve significant improvement."

In 1969 Pope conducted an interesting experiment known as operant conditioning, or the use of token economies. Tokens were used to reinforce desirable conduct such as the care of one's room, personal grooming, and ceasing to mutter. The "rewards" or tokens were given for positive acts; the tokens themselves could be exchanged for a visit to the Snack Bar or Sundry Shop, a visit with a volunteer, or a trip to the library. Every day the patient's activities were reviewed with him, and he was given his tokens and his "shopping list" of privileges. Positive results were tangible. One patient ceased to mutter as he walked the corridors or grounds, another one stuck to his work therapy, and another went willingly to occupational therapy, activities on which he could not previously concentrate.

Dr. Rolfe Finn returned to Sheppard Pratt in 1963 to head the newly created Activities Department. In placing a senior psychiatrist in charge of the new department, Gibson wrote, "We are convinced that the environment plays an important, sometimes crucial, role in the recovery of patients...For environmental therapy to be truly effective, it must be closely coordinated with psychotherapy under the leadership of an experienced psychiatrist." Mrs.

Anne Taliaferro, a Registered Occupational Therapist with long experience, continued as Assistant Director under Finn, and later under Jerome Levin, MA, a clinical psychologist who joined the staff as Director in 1968.

After examining, evaluating and rethinking previous activities, a new program was developed. During the mornings, each patient was assigned to a specific therapy of his own choosing. The afternoon program consisted of a broad array of hobby interests and recreation. The possibilities, which were extensive, included all the crafts associated with occupational therapy, plus beginning music, guitar, intermediate bridge, yoga, billiards, and drama; and, in recreation, many gymnasium and field sports, plus the use of the pool. The latter was made possible by the construction in 1966 of a well-equipped, all-year-round swimming pool, 35 feet wide by 75 feet long, with ample room for dressing rooms and an area for social activites. The pool was dedicated to William Rush Dunton, Jr., MD, "an enthusiastic pioneer and founder of Occupational Therapy at Sheppard Pratt...1895-1924."

Sunday afternoon services were held in the chapel, led for many years by the Reverend W. C. Roberts and the Reverend Philip Kingsley Smith of Trinity Episcopal Church of Towson, and by the Reverend Roger W. Fink of First Lutheran Church of Towson. By request of the younger patients, these services were changed to 6:30 P.M. and were followed by informal discussions after each service, plus a Coke hour. Roman Catholic Communion services were conducted once a week, with a preparatory meeting led by a seminarian. On the Jewish holidays, appropriate celebrations were conducted, usually by Rabbi Benjamin Bak of the Jewish Family and Children's Service. A successful Bible Study Group, held one evening a week in the winter season, was led by the Reverend Arthur Urie and the Reverend Barrett Rudd of Towson Presbyterian Church.

The Constitution of the Patient-Staff Council, prepared in 1962 and revised several times, stated that the Council was created to make a favorable and orderly channel of communication between patients and staff concerning the welfare and interests of the Hospital community; to promote the exchange of ideas and sentiments among the patients; and to execute directives initiated by the Council and approved by the Staff. It consisted of members elected by the patients from each hall and staff representatives including medical, nursing and occupational therapy departments. In addition to being a center for discussion, the Council arranged for much needed evening programs, and events off the grounds such as bowling, skating, city tours, and trips to major athletic events. The Council had several subcommittees, including a social issues group and a religious committee.

The Patient-Staff Council's weekly news publication contained current events, notices of committee meetings, reports of their activities, grievances and complaints, an activities schedule for the week, both within the hospital and on the outside, drawings, book reviews, poems, an occasional questionnaire, and the menu for the week. Sometimes ideas suggested were impractical or nontherapeutic, but the Council was an excellent medium for patient expression and played an important part in the life of the Hospital.

Along with other therapies and activities in the early 1960's, Thomas M. Green of the Baltimore County School System conducted educational work on both the high school and college levels at Sheppard Pratt. In 1964, Mrs. Michelina Hudak joined him to teach English and mathematics to six high-school age young people. Her pupils increased to 14

the next year. Two of these students passed the High School Equivalency Test for a County diploma. Two young patients also attended classes in the Towson Senior High School. In 1967, 19 patients were enrolled in classes for three hours daily, and Mr. Green's pupils numbered 12. With additional adolescents residing in the Hospital, the number of students grew. In 1967-68, 40 students participated in the high school academic year, and 20 in the summer school program. There were then five teachers under the direction of Mrs. Patricia Dockendorf, who served as Coordinator. In 1968-69, Mr. Richard R. Giasson, MA, an experienced teacher and educational administrator, joined the staff as Director of Secondary and Adult Education. The enrollment of students in 1968-69 reached 66, with 27 different courses of study offered. New school rooms were completed on the ground floor of the Chapman Building, including a science laboratory and a library. The school, now officially known as Mt. Airy High School, was tentatively accredited by the Baltimore County Department of Education. At the Commencement in June of 1970, 13 were granted diplomas. Several of the group were admitted to collegiate institutions for the fall of 1970.

Mt. Airy Junior-Senior High School was the keystone for the teenaged persons in the milieu that Sheppard Pratt combined with individual and group psychotherapy. "School is a sensible occupation for adolescents," said Giasson. "It prevents moping or resisting contrived occupational therapy...It keeps the youngster from falling behind his peers scholastically. For those who are not well enough or have retrogressed in their therapy, there is a tutorial program set up in various halls three times a week. For others who lack confidence to go into a normal school situation or the ability to compete in such a setting, there is a special education class."

All the school attenders were inpatients in 1969-70 except four, who were formerly in the Hospital. The students were above average mentally, with intelligence quotients of 110 to 140. Rebelling against their families and society in general, their anti-establishment feelings were exaggerated because of their emotional problems, and the fact that more than half had experimented with drugs. Diagnostically, most were classified as having personality disorders.

Of this department of the Hospital, Dr. Gibson said, "Many factors are involved in the increase in adolescents being admitted...Numerically, there are more teenagers in our population, so one would expect more psychiatric problems. There is also an increased awareness that certain behavioral problems are more than delinquency. Parents and their teenagers are more receptive to the idea that there may be a psychiatric discorder present that warrants hospital treatment...The adolescent is the most vulnerable in our population. They are called upon to assume responsibilities that are often equal to those we expect from an adult. They are exposed to a great many stresses. At the same time, they have not developed the skills and stability of personality structure to cope with these things adequately. Thus, if the population in general goes through a state of tension and upheaval, one of the first groups that will show symptomatic behavior would be the adolescent group."

Through the 1960's, the Child Guidance Clinic continued its useful work under the able direction of Dr. Kathryn L. Schultz and Dr. Genieann P. Patton. In an average year, 250 interviews were held with children and their parents. The program expanded when Dr. James J. Gibbs became Director of the Department of Child Psychiatry in 1966. Gibbs, of Wayne University College of Medicine in Detroit,

RIGHT: *A student in the Forbush Children's Center doing his lessons. Formerly the Mt. Airy School, the Forbush Center is now located in Chapman South.*
OPPOSITE LEFT: *Relaxing over the pool table in the Ford Recreational Building.*
LEFT: *A young artist at work in the Forbush Center.*

received his psychiatric training at Letterman General Hospital in San Francisco and the Children's Hospital of the District of Columbia. He came to Sheppard Pratt from the position of Chief of Children's Psychiatric Services of the Walter Reed Hospital in Washington, DC. He proceeded to develop and diversify child psychiatric activities necessary to support a training program in child psychiatry, and to provide residents in adult psychiatry with proper exposure to childhood mental disorders. Dr. Emilio Dominguez and Dr. Jaime Lievano, both trained at the Menninger Clinic, were added.

In the fall of 1967, a Children's Day Care Program for emotionally disturbed young school-age children had opened. The children received individual therapy while their families were involved in intensive case work. The western section of the ground floor of the Chapman Building, once an occupational therapy area, was made into attractive rooms for this new service; the Child Guidance Clinic also moved into new quarters in the same building. Miss Jeanne Curran enthusiastically directed the Day Care Program, where eight children were enrolled.

In October of 1969, an Adult Day Care Center was opened in recently modernized rooms on the west side of Windy Brae. This center was created to give support to outgoing patients, and to provide an alternate for those mentally disturbed who needed more than out patient care but not full inpatient attention. Patients continued to live at home. The Center got off to a slow start because the psychiatric profession in Baltimore had little acquaintance with this new possibility of care.

The Psychiatric Emergency Service and Crisis Intervention Clinic, the last of the new programs planned in the sixties, was opened in cooperation with Greater Baltimore Medical Center and St. Joseph's Hospital in 1970. Under a grant from the State, this service was designed to provide care for psychiatric emergencies on a 24-hour-per-day, seven-day-a-week basis, to residents of the northern area of Baltimore County. The Crisis Clinic was staffed by Dr. Samuel Blumenfeld and Dr. Arthur Hildreth, psychiatrists, a social worker, and a mental health technician. Resident psychiatrists from Sheppard Pratt provided coverage during hours when the Clinic was not open under the guiding psychiatrists. The method of treatment was short-term, aimed at alleviating the immediate problem and the institution of more adaptive treatment, if necessary, elsewhere.

In 1967, a new Department of Medicine was established, with Dr. Newland E. Day as Chief of Service, ably assisted in day-to-day activities by Miss Reba Hilliard, Medical Assistant, and Margaret Protzman, LPN. A new set of offices was built on the ground floor of the A Building. A group of medical consultants associated with the Hospital gave, in a typical year, 350 ophthamology examinations, 350 dental examinations, and 300 gynecology examinations. Electrocardiograms were taken for 120 patients and 10 employees, nearly 1,000 x-ray pictures were taken; almost 5,000 laboratory tests were processed. The department was responsible for the personal health of the institution, for emergency treatment, and for the screening of new employees.

Through the creation of new departments, there were increasing demands on both the medical and patient libraries. There were 3,432 volumes in the medical library with a circulation of a thousand volumes a year, and 6,000 in the patient library with a circulation of approximately 3,000. Mrs. Jean Husman was librarian of both divisions, and provided the staff with reference material, bibliographic items and interlibrary loans.

18. Preparation for Future Development

FOR MANY YEARS, the administrative, or supportive, services of the Hospital lagged behind the professional departments. The latter always enjoyed an enviable reputation, but Maintenance, Personnel Administration, Purchasing and related functions were slow to respond to the rapid pace of the Departments of Psychiatry, Nursing, etc. To some degree this had an adverse effect on the treatment of patients. This was evident to Francis E. Lambert soon after his appointment as Administrative Officer in 1965. Under Lambert were placed all the nonclinical activities except the Financial Department, which reported directly to the Trustees. Lambert began his duties with enthusiasm and proceeded to reorganize the various services. He was assisted by Community Systems Foundation, a nonprofit group of efficiency engineers who made recommendations for greater utility.

Under Lambert's supervision a Policy Book, subject to constant revision, was prepared, covering such matters as vacation pay, sick leave, grievance procedures, guidelines for civil disturbances, and other items not mentioned in the Employees' Handbook. An inventory of all Hospital equipment and furniture was taken by an outside firm, all pieces of furniture tagged with location indicated, and a property control center established. A personnel consultant was employed who studied the wage and salary scale of Sheppard Pratt, made comparisons with other Baltimore hospitals, and recommended changes. The minimum wage was raised within a few years from $1.39 an hour to $2.25, while the annual average wage scale rose from $3,122 in 1960 to $3,835 in 1964 and to $6,033 in 1969. For example, in 1969 the starting salary for nurses was $7,300. A job description of every position was made, and twice a year individual evaluations instituted through department heads. Merit increases were given when recommended. The number of employees at the Hospital increased from 375 in 1960, to 433 in 1964, and to 544 in 1969.

One of Lambert's fortunate appointments was that of John Moro as Plant Manager. Moro, an excellent planner and organizer, directed the efforts of the various craftsmen with great skill. His previous experience in renovating an old hospital prepared him for the exacting task of repairs and renovations at Sheppard Pratt, often of an emergency nature. With skilled mechanics, Moro was able to create new rooms for enlarged programs from out-of-the-way areas little used or long forgotten. Increased attention was given to safety precautions, and the number of accidents to employees reduced to such an extent that insurance was reduced by $8,000 a year. Security measures were expanded, the force of guards doubled, and the large iron gates at the Gatehouse closed at 10 P.M. — for the first time in many decades. A Supervisor of Security was appointed, and a committee, which made a thorough inspection of the entire Hospital once a month, established.

Fire drills, always held regularly, now became more systematized; additional alarm boxes were provided, and an automatic fire-detection system installed in some areas. The fire brigade was enlarged, better fire-fighting equipment secured, and every employee required to take fire-fighting instructions under the direction of the County Fire Deparment.

During the latter part of the 1960's, there were many physical improvements made, including air conditioning the Chapman and the Service Buildings, and placing window air conditioners in most offices. Attractive lamp posts were placed along the main roads and in the parking areas. The barn, now without livestock, was remodelled into craft and maintenance shops at a cost of $150,000. The former paint and carpentry shop over the garage

BELOW: *The north facade of the main complex, showing how the New Central Building harmonized with the architecture of the earlier Victorian A and B Buildings.*

LEFT: *Dr. Gibson with Medical Directors and Administrators of the "Ivy League Hospitals."*
OPPOSITE: *Artist Aaron Sopher looks at a staff lecture.*
OPPOSITE BELOW: *Sopher catches a young girl taking out her aggressions on the punching bag, circa 1970. Today the large gym in Chapman South offers manyfold the athletic opportunities that patients and staff formerly enjoyed at Sheppard Pratt.*

became the receiving center for all incoming goods. With increased numbers of employees, patients and visitors, five large parking areas had to be built.

"It is a tribute to the architects and builders of early times that Sheppard Pratt Hospital has served the increasing and changing needs of its patients so well." Although the foundations and walls were as sturdy as ever, the utilities were not. Water lines were clogged with rust, sewer pipes were no longer adequate, and with the addition of air conditioners, television sets, electric typewriters, and other such equipment, there was insufficient power to keep them all in operation. In 1966, the engineering firm of Fred von Behren, Inc. was employed to make a survey of the entire plant, and by the next year reports were presented covering the electrical, hot and cold water, fire protection, natural gas and steam distribution, air conditioning and ventilation systems. With these reports before it, the Property Committee spent many sessions considering whether to recommend abandoning the ancient plant, or remodeling it. The buildings were so well suited to the purpose for which they were constructed, with large rooms, wide corridors, and high windows, that it was decided to renovate the interiors and add a new building if necessary. Contracts were let for the renovation of outside utilities, and for many months the campus was laced with trenches while pipes and wires were replaced. As areas were remodeled, new electrical panels were installed. The long tunnels under the A and B Buildings containing a miscellaneous collection of pipes and wires were made safe, all valves labeled and new panels installed. In a period of five years, more than a million dollars were spent on improvements.

Now it was decided to construct a new building in front of the Service Building, which would blend in a pleasing manner with the older structures, to contain new offices, kitchens and dining rooms, and air conditioning equipment sufficient for the main complex. Anthony J. Ianniello, AIA, now joined von Behren for the major designing. The low bid for the construction of the new Central Building, made by MacLeod Construction Company, amounted to $2,252,030. On May 13, 1969 the cornerstone was laid by Maryland Governor Marvin Mandel and the President of the Board, in the presence of Trustees, employees and friends.

For some time, the third and fourth floors of the A and B Buildings had been little used, and it was decided to renovate these while the Central Building was being constructed. In these areas were one hundred rooms which would make, with new lighting, floor coverings, and air conditioning, excellent quarters for doctors, medical library, and research accommodations. They would be made accessible by adding elevators, necessary for adequate use. This renovation added a cost of approximately a million dollars to the building program.

To help with the construction costs, the Trustees decided to appeal to the general public for funds, something never attempted before. A well-known firm of fund raisers was employed, and Mr. John E. Motz, a Trustee well versed in fund raising techniques, consented to head the development drive. Several hundred thousand dollars were raised. The trouble was that times were not propitious, and it was soon discovered that people in general considered Sheppard Pratt a wealthy corporation, its original endowment largely increased by purchases of land made by Towson State University. Thus the Trustees realized the securing of funds from individuals and foundations would necessarily be a long-term project.

At this juncture it was felt wise to increase the size of the Board of Trustees, an idea suggested long

before by Dr. Kubie and Mr. Berkeley Mann. The National Hospital Association had for many years advocated that the medical staffs be represented on the Trustee Boards, so the first new member elected was Dr. Gibson; Dr. Philip Wagley, a prominent Baltimore physician, president-elect of the Baltimore Medical Society; and James D. Peacock, senior partner at Semmes, Bowen, and Semmes were also chosen. The addition of these three younger men brought new strength to the Trustees.

An *ex efficio* member, whom it was always pleasant to have at the sessions of the Board, was Mrs. William P. Horton, the President of the Auxiliary. The Auxiliary, which evolved from the earlier Women's Board, steadily gained momentum as it discovered how to be useful to the Hosptial.

For the first five years of the 1960's, Sheppard Pratt operated at a loss; in the last half, because of outside grants and a much larger endowment income, the books were balanced and a sum set aside each year for modernization and new building. Grants from the United States Public Health Bureau for the training of psychiatrists increased from $11,300 in 1960 to $252,457 in 1968-1969. Chiefly due to the sale of land to the State, the endowment income grew from $197,610 in 1960 to $432,250 in 1968-69. In that year the Trustees directed that half the income from the endowment be used for grants-in-aid, and half set aside for modernization and new construction. A Grant-in-Aid Committee met each month to pass on all requests for assistance. The budget for 1969-70 was over six million dollars, and that for 1970-71 was $7,350,000. This large increase was mainly due to rising wages and salaries and the cost of employee benefits.

In the spring of 1970, Dr. Gibson was honored as the recipient of the Edward A. Strecker, MD, Award as the Young Psychiatrist of the Year, from the In-

stitute of the Pennsylvania Hospital to "an individual who has made an outstanding contribution in the field of psychiatric care and treatment." He was also singularly honored in May by his election to a three-year term as a member of the Board of Trustees of the American Psychiatric Association, and was named to the Executive Committee. Not many months previously, Gibson had been elected to the Baltimore County Board of Health — the first psychiatrist so named — which put him in the center of the health movement in the County. Dr. Whitmarsh became President of the Maryland Psychology Association; Dr. James R. Ralph became editor of the *Newsletter* of the Black Psychiatrist Association; and Dr. Kent Robinson, a member of the Group for the Advancement of Psychiatry and Chairman of the Advisory Council for the Mental Hygiene Association of the State Board of Health. Mr. Leon, Director of Community Relations and Development, received the Silver Anvil Award of the Public Relations Society of America for outstanding work in this area.

The Joint Conference of Staff and Trustees raised many interesting questions:

- Under the concept of "team work" in the treatment of patients, to what extent does the nurse become a therapist?
- Does Sheppard Pratt need "a breathing spell" before undertaking further new programs?
- Do adolescents who have experimented with drugs belong in a psychiatric hospital?
- Can more useful work and vocational programs be devised for adolescents?
- Do some of the current projects at Sheppard Pratt have potential research value, and, if so, how shall the data be gathered?
- Should Sheppard Pratt establish its own half-way house, removed from the Hospital grounds, and under controls not found in the usual half-way house?
- Could former patients be utilized in treatment programs?
- Community health programs by-pass the chronic patient. What can Sheppard Pratt do to meet this need? Should the pilot project conducted by Dr. Murdock be revived?

In his annual report to the Board in May of 1970, Gibson summed up the activities of the Hospital during its first 70 years (1891-1960):

"Sheppard Pratt devoted its efforts almost exclusively to an adult inpatient psychiatric service with no reference to the immediate community. Educational programs for mental health professionals were conducted, but probably in the main as a method of providing the services to the patient. The quality of the services was generally high and for the most part stayed within the mainstream of general psychiatric practice. Research of an organized type was done in the early days but did not receive consistent emphasis...Community involvement was not emphasized...and appears to have been one of minimal interaction characteristic of most hospitals prior to 1960."

From 1970 on, programs at Sheppard Pratt would include patient care, teaching, research, and community outreach. It was assumed that the patient population would average 250, divided into five active services and two custodial services: "208 would be patients receiving active treatment with individual psychotherapy; 12 patients would be considered as receiving treatment on the active services, but not having individual psychotherapy, and being under the care of the Service Chief; 30 patients would be in the custodial groups, most elderly and with a significant number of infirm...Since individual

therapy is only one aspect of the treatment provided by physicians,...there are nine therapy groups... which in round numbers would handle about 80 patients in group therapy.''

Hardly significant before 1965, but now disturbingly on the increase, was the admission of so many adolescents and young adults, amounting in 1970 to between 75 and 85. Since approximately half of these young people had experimented with drugs, new approaches had to be devised and their success was not yet assured.

Teaching programs at Sheppard Pratt for the growing body of residents, psychiatric nurses, and for graduate students in social work, psychology and education increased. In 1970 the Trustees approved in principal the establishment of a School for Allied Mental Health Services, which would coordinate all the existing programs and promote and develop the role of Sheppard Pratt as a teaching institution. Research was placed on a permanent foundation with the appointment of Dr. Whitmarsh as Director, and useful projects were planned for the future.

A new area of development was greater involvement in the community, both a challenge and a responsibility. Work with the colleges and neighboring hospitals, the Training School for Boys, the Police Department, the outpatient services for adults and children, the Mt. Airy School (which enrolled some outpatients), and the Emergency Crisis Clinic established in 1970 — all were outgrowths of this new outreach philosophy. In 1970 a grant was received from the State to study the feasibility of placing on the grounds, and under the management of the Hospital, a Comprehensive Community Mental Health Clinic. Gibson reported to the Trustees, "The potential desirable programs will always far exceed the capabilities of the Institution," but that the Hospital should advance as funds are available.

OPPOSITE TOP: *Working with a felt board in the Forbush Children's Center.*
TOP: *Staff and visitors at the 1974 Mental Health Fair.*
ABOVE: *A teacher works with a reading group in the Forbush Center.*

19. Patients as Consumers

DURING THE 1970's Sheppard Pratt witnessed and was a part of a new era in health care provision. For the first time in medical history, patients were now identified as consumers. With this shift from "patient" to "consumer" came fundamental changes in the philosophy of the American health care system. Where before leadership and responsibility for health care rested solely with health professionals and providers, the 1970's ushered in the age of outside regulation by government, private insurers, and consumer agencies.

Many of the changes in the health care system were directly related to the inflationary cost of care and increased political and governmental influences. In 1965, the last year before the government enacted Medicare and Medicaid, $39 billion was spent on health care in the United States ($200 per capita) claiming 5.9% of the gross national product with public dollars accounting for 25% of the total. Ten years later, in 1975, expenditures totaled $118 billion ($550 per capita), claiming 8.3% of the GNP with public dollars accounting for 42%.

The first piece of legislation introduced to the House of Representatives in 1973 read: "Recognizing that health care is an inherent right of each individual and of all the people of the United States...the Congress finds and declares that health services must be so organized and financed as to make them readily available to all; and that it is a function of the government to insure that these ends are attained." Adequate health care was declared a right of each individual. Yet making good on this commitment would not only be enormously expensive, but because of the highly speculative character of emotional disorders, psychiatric care was left particularly vulnerable to challenge. It was no longer the case that health care could be judged by health professionals. It was feared that concern for the individual

patient might be lost when overemphasis was placed on cost effectiveness. To protect the inherent rights of Sheppard Pratt patients to high quality mental health care, the Hospital had to develop responsive, internally managed programs capable of more efficiently controlling the distribution, quality and cost of health care, and, most importantly, of demonstrating the effectiveness of treatment. Gibson explained, "The tendency to think of mental disorders and their treatment as falling wholly outside the mainstream of medical care has fostered such clear-cut discrimination against the mentally ill, that organized psychiatry has long been in the posture of having to demonstrate cost consciousness and to show that psychiatric illness can be treated within reasonable limits."

The Social Security Amendments of 1972 established a Professional Standards Review Organization (PSRO) to set up a formal system for physicians to monitor health services. Thus, Sheppard Pratt, like hospitals across the country, began gearing up for the new era of increased accountability and regulation. In order to comply with new health care regulations, evaluative research of patient care was necessary. Studies aimed at measuring the effectiveness of treatment and the productivity of therapeutic programs would provide vital information and enable Sheppard Pratt to get hard data in areas where before only clinical impressions were available. The first step taken by Sheppard Pratt was to establish the Office of Patient Care Assessment as the administrative center for all patient care review activities.

The responsibilities of the new Patient Care Assessment Office were great, and included such tasks as collecting and analyzing patient data; developing criteria for measuring quality of care; coordinating existing internal review functions;

developing reporting systems necessary to keep the Board of Trustees, Medical Staff and Administration informed about the quality of care; and developing and maintaining relationships with external surveillance agencies – including the Joint Commission, the Social Security Administration, the State Mental Health Administration and private insurers. In dealing with inpatient services, the Office of Patient Care Assessment was also responsible for reviewing all elective and emergency admissions and conducting quality and utilization reviews throughout a patient's stay in accordance with a pre-planned time schedule. Ultimately, the goal of the Patient Care Assessment Office would be to provide the data needed to demonstrate the effectiveness of the Hospital's patient care.

The need for more accurate and more easily understood medical records became critical, and would serve as the base for the efficient operation of the Office of Patient Care Assessment. A new system of orienting all Sheppard Pratt patient records to problems and their solutions was initiated. The key to the system was a problem list which served much like a table of contents. For each problem, a treatment plan was constructed. Progress notes were arranged by problem title and number so that problems and treatments were clearly linked. This format made it much easier to understand the total needs of the patient, and enabled all members of the treatment team to add integrated information to the chart. By contrast, the old system, more often than not, was no system at all; instead it had been a random sequence of isolated findings, anecdotes, and thus, speculations.

With all the new regulations and the reams of paper work that went with them, accountability for patient care clearly rested on efficient data collection, storage, and retrieval systems. Under the direc-

TOP: *The Auxiliary Gift Shop on the first floor of the Activities Building. A large variety of supplies, cards and periodicals can be purchased by patients and staff. Composed of outside volunteers, the Auxiliary donates much-needed vehicles, equipment and services.*
ABOVE: *Additional efforts of the Auxiliary: the Employee Christmas Party.*

ABOVE RIGHT: *Dr. Gibson, as he appeared at a Board meeting in the early seventies.*
ABOVE LEFT: *President of the Board John Luetkemeyer, in the mid-seventies.*
BELOW: *The Powerplant, which generated the Hospital's energy needs until Sheppard Pratt switched over to Baltimore Gas & Electric. Today it serves as a laundry and garage.*

tion of Gerald A. Whitmarsh, PhD, the Shepard Pratt Research Department developed three such systems.

The first, a patient-based system, allowed studies of treatment effectiveness and cost efficiency. Admission, treatment, and discharge information was used for program evaluation and studies of treatment outcome. The second system documented clinical staff time by specific patients and specific treatment modalities. Actual services rendered by social workers, medical staff, residents, psychologists and members of the environmental therapy staff were all documented. The final system incorporated studies in performance, utilization and cost factors of all Hospital departments, clinical and non-clinical. Significantly, each of these three research systems was a pioneering effort in the assessment of psychiatric programs. By contrast, few attempts had been made in the past to demonstrate the efficacy of psychiatric treatment programs.

These research and documentation programs at the Hospital were developed none too soon. Regulation by outside agencies continued to escalate to the extent that in 1975 the New York State Hospital Association Task Force found that *no less than 164 different regulatory agencies had some jurisdiction over hospitals in the state.* Of those regulatory agencies, no less than 25 separate agencies reviewed hospital admitting procedures, 33 protected patient rights and 31 ensured patients' safety. In reply to the ever increasing regulations, Dr. Gibson wrote in the 1975-76 Annual Report, ''Critical policy decisions are being made by state and federal administrators, third-party payers, the courts, and the consumers. Although well-intentioned, such individuals and groups seldom have clinical experience — and worse yet, they are sometimes insensitive to the needs of the mentally ill.''

Third-party payers held a powerful influence on

LEFT: *The Gazebo, one of Sheppard Pratt's earliest structures intended to help give the campus a park-like atmosphere for patients and staff. As it looked in the mid-seventies.* **BELOW:** *The year-round swimming pool, constructed in 1966, is continually a source of relaxation for patients and staff. It was dedicated to William Rush Dunton, founder of Occupational Therapy at the Hospital.*

ABOVE: *Mental Health Fair 1974, co-sponsored by Sheppard Pratt and the Mental Health Association of Metropolitan Baltimore. Here Dr. Gibson gives an informal talk on depression.*
RIGHT: *Finding a good buy at the Auxiliary Bargain Basement, located in the basement of the Casino.*

LEFT: *Mid-seventies Board meeting. From foreground, clockwise: John Luetkemeyer, Dr. Gibson, James Peacock, Samuel Hopkins.*

mental health services. Because of the volume of claims, they began utilizing nonphysician reviewers to screen medical records in accordance with established guidelines. One set of guidelines contained such statements as, "Psychiatry does not have the definitive structure of medical science. It is composed of multiple philosophical disciplines with little agreement on methods of practice and a diffusion of contentious theories on the ideology and treatment of mental conditions." The justifiable fear of the mental health providers, as Gibson explained, was that, "The use of such guidelines might lead to the denial of treatment to hundreds or perhaps thousands of patients. The short term effect would be bad enough, but consider what would happen to the future of all mental health care." Gibson warned, "If mental health professionals fail to act, we will lose all meaningful influence on the quality of treatment and the manner in which services are provided. We must serve as advocates to ensure that those suffering from psychiatric and related disorders will receive adequate treatment."

Because of his conviction that peer review was essential in fulfilling this responsibility to patients, in 1976, as President of the American Psychiatric Association (APA), Gibson conducted a conference on professional responsibility and peer review in psychiatry. The conference brought together as participants psychiatrists concerned with self-evaluation, consumer representatives, third-party payers and quality assurance experts. Each group judged whether peer review as then conducted by the APA was on the right track, how the system could be improved, and whether it met the needs of concerned groups. Through a grant from the Board of Trustees of the APA, a report on the conference was prepared and distributed to the 23,000 members of the APA and to 15,000 other professionals and in-

dividuals interested in mental health services.

Despite the difficulties imposed by regulation, the early 1970's proved a time of great expansion in services offered by Sheppard Pratt. In 1972, John A. Luetkemeyer was elected the new President of the Board of Trustees, and under his leadership the Hospital began the renovation of the old Service Building. When completed, the modernization of the building would provide recreation, social and occupational therapy facilities for the patients, as well as significantly enhance the activities portion of their overall treatment program. Plans for the renovation of the first and second floors of the A and B Buildings were finalized, and work began.

Adolescent admissions, which began to increase in the mid-sixties, continued their steady rise. In 1966 the adolescent population of the Hospital was 10%, with 54 patients under the age of 19 admitted. By contrast, in 1976, adolescent inpatient admissions totaled almost 27% of the Hospital population, with 183 patients 19 years and younger admitted during the year. In response to these increased admissions, the Hospital expanded services offered to the youngsters. A young adolescent service provided intensive, comprehensive residential care for disturbed youngsters from ages 12 to 15. Though organized for an optimal stay of six to 12 months, the Hospital also accepted patients for evaluation and brief crisis-oriented treatment. Through individual psychotherapy, casework with parents, family meetings, and related efforts, the adolescent unit's multidisciplinary staff helped hundreds of youngsters sublimate instinctive drives, gain self-respect, adapt to the stresses of everyday living, participate in meaningful personal relationships, and progress toward fulfilling their intellectual potential.

Towards that end, in 1972 the Mt. Airy School, already accredited as a nonpublic secondary school,

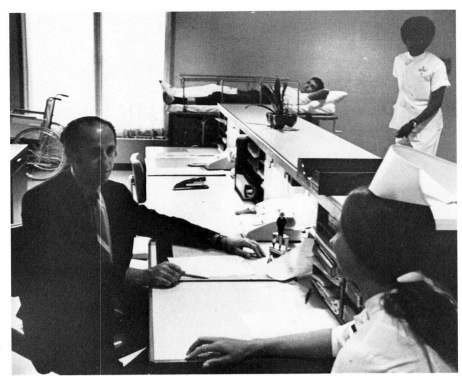

RIGHT: *Dr. Blumenfeld at a nurses' station in 1971.*
BELOW: *NORCOM Open House. Left to right: Drs. Bendit, Blumenfeld, Yeganeh; Marge Wisnom.*

was now granted full accreditation by the Maryland State Department of Education as a nonpublic secondary school for the emotionally handicapped. During the year, the school switched to a full 12-month, four-quarter calendar, offering more than 25 credit courses for students in grades 7 through 12. More day students were admitted, some of whom were in the school on an aftercare basis, having previously been enrolled as inpatients. That same year, the Sheppard Pratt day program for young children was dedicated to the President Emeritus of the Board of Trustees and his wife. The Bliss and Laverne Forbush Center provided an educational and therapeutic program for children 6 through 12 who, because of emotional disturbance, were unable to benefit from a normal classroom setting but were not so severely disturbed that they required hospitalization. After the Forbush Center reached its enrollment goal of 18, the Hospital started another after-school program for children in public schools. Because learning and behavioral problems were recognized as the two main sources of trouble, the program was designed to provide individualized attention with emphasis on reading and group interaction skills for children who demonstrated difficulties adjusting to school.

Through the efforts of many, the Mt. Airy School and the Bliss and Laverne Forbush Center accomplished much in the education of elementary and high school students. But services for those children of middle school age were lacking. Thus, in 1978 the Mt. Airy School and the Forbush Center were formally joined to one school with separate divisions for elementary, middle and secondary instruction. The curriculum of the secondary school division was upgraded and now included work-study programs, courses in industrial arts and basic education classes for learning-disabled students. With the reorganization, four new staff positions

TOP: *A senior citizen visits the Geriatric Day Treatment Center. Through its Outpatient Services, Sheppard Pratt has been able to help tens of thousands better cope with their lives.*
ABOVE: *The park-like atmosphere of the Hospital campus is conducive to relaxing chats.*

RIGHT: *A pensive staffer, circa 1975.*
OPPOSITE: *An emotional mother gives her child a hug for a morning send-off at the Forbush School.*
OPPOSITE BOTTOM: *Children working with papier-mache at the Mt. Airy (now Forbush) School; as interpreted by Aaron Sopher.*

were formed. A social work associate was needed to serve both day students and their families. A resource teacher provided academic and behavior crisis support to students at all levels. Coordination of work-study programs and class placement and scheduling was handled by the new guidance counselor. And a speech therapist carried out testing as well as individual and group therapy sessions.

During the same year, the Children's Inpatient Unit, which operated for some years only five days per week, with children returning home for weekends, was expanded to become a seven-day per week operation. Although this expansion required more nursing staff and other program increases, the Hospital believed the change helped the unit in responding more fully to the needs of patients and also enabled the Hospital to admit a wider variety of young patients from a greater geographical area.

Undoubtedly, the most heartening and encouraging events in the early 70's came in the area of community service. In 1972 the efforts of countless physicians and staff members in various community outreach programs received national recognition: Sheppard Pratt was awarded the American Psychiatric Association's Gold Achievement Award "for demonstrating how a private hospital can modify its traditional role and become a catalyst in the development of community services."

The first community programs initiated by the Hospital were characterized by an extension of the institution's existing programs and services to the surrounding community. Work with neighboring colleges and hospitals, the Training School for Boys, and the Police Department, as well as the Hospital's outpatient services for adults and children, were all examples of this first wave of community outreach. As this type of work expanded, a new dimension of community service was added. The Hospital began

new programs in conjunction with representatives of the specific community which would be served.

At the request of the state, one of the first examples of this extended work with the community was the Hospital's Comprehensive Drug Abuse Program (COMDAP). Under the direction of William E. Abramson MD, the COMDAP program utilized social, psychological and vocational rehabilitation methods coupled with methadone chemotherapy. From its initial weeks of operation providing services to the Baltimore County judicial system, COMDAP saw increasing numbers of referrals from both the courts and the jails. Soon the judicially-based operation was expanded to take on the responsibility of evaluating individuals being considered for parole, who, as a condition of their parole, were to be admitted into a drug program. In a short time, COMDAP's judicial evaluation and jail detoxification projects became models for other programs, and COMDAP received the highest rating in an evaluation by the State's Drug Abuse Administration. In 1977, after five and a half years of operating out of two locations, COMDAP was moved into newly renovated quarters in the main Hospital complex. This new consolidated area enabled the program to provide an even more integrated treatment service and to initiate the COMDAP Educational Advancement Program. A highly innovative patient-operated service, the new program assisted patients in obtaining general equivalency diplomas and financial assistance for college attendance.

The largest number of patients served through a single outpatient program in 1977 was admitted into the Northern Baltimore County Community Mental Health Program (NORCOM). This program was begun in 1974 under the direction of Robert Temple, MD, and was a comprehensive program run in conjunction with the Baltimore County Mental

aaron sopher

Health Clinics. NORCOM provided outpatient services and 24 hour per day, 7 day per week crisis and emergency care. During the year, 1,655 patients were admitted, most in need of some financial assistance.

In August of 1977, the Hospital further expanded its outpatient programs to include services designed for the elderly residents of the community. The only program of its kind in the area, the Hospital's Geriatric Day Treatment Program provided individual, family and group therapy, social work services, community orientation and specialized activity therapy groups specific to the needs of the area's geriatric population.

During 1977 Sheppard Pratt's varied inpatient and community programs would serve in excess of 4,300 persons. The Hospital was greatly assisted in this work by 325 volunteers who donated over 30,000 hours in no less than 31 Hospital inpatient and outpatient departments. That same year, through their efforts in managing The Gatehouse Shoppe, the Hospital Auxiliary was able to donate much needed equipment for patient use in the Activity Therapy Department and the Adolescent Activity Center. The previous year the Auxiliary, headed by Mrs. Lee C. Park and Mrs. Robert L. Randolph, generated enough funds to present the Hospital with a van for use in connection with patient activities.

In thanking all the workers who so freely donated their time, John Luetkemeyer spoke for all the members of the Hospital staff when he said, "Such assistance, although very valuable in dollars, is, even more important in those tremendous human satisfactions that come not only to the patient, but also to the volunteer."

After annual giving began in 1972, contributions broke each past year's records. In 1977 these donations exceeded $68,000 and provided the equivalent income of an additional $1,200,000 endowment.

Also in 1977, the Hospital established a pooled income fund for deferred gifts to Sheppard Pratt. To encourage gifts from those who need the current income from funds they could eventually give to the Hospital, the new program provided these donors with current tax credits on deferred gifts.

That same year the Hospital received the most substantial gift since the landmark bequests of Moses Sheppard and Enoch Pratt. Through the bequest of Jesse Goldman, Sheppard Pratt received an unrestricted gift of over $425,000. The Board designated that the principal of the Goldman bequest be added to funds acting as endowment and that the income be used to help meet the need for financial assistance to patients in the Day/Evening Treatment Program.

Along with the generous gift of Jesse Goldman, other milestones marked by the Hospital in the decade included the death of Sheppard Pratt's oldest living alumnus, Dr. Clarance B. Farrar, in June of 1970. Farrar had succeeded Dr. Brush as Editor-in-Chief of the *American Psychiatric Journal*, and with his death was lost one of the major figures of the early period of the Hospital.

October 27, 1973 marked the death of Dr. Lawrence S. Kubie. A member of the Sheppard Pratt staff for 14 years, Kubie was the author of some 335 scientific articles, many of which dealt with his interest in furthering the evolution of psychoanalytical theory. Kubie also served for nine years as the Editor-in-Chief of the *Journal of Nervous and Mental Disease*. Upon his death, Kubie bequeathed his personal library of over 14,000 volumes to Sheppard Pratt's medical library. This contribution of shared knowledge for generations to come spoke very eloquently of the manner in which Kubie lived. Truly he was a man dedicated to the growth and enrichment of all he met.

OPPOSITE: *Louis Goldstein, Comptroller of the State of Maryland, speaks at the 125th Anniversary celebration.*
RIGHT: *COMDAP employees at a staff session.*

As the number of outpatient services increased, the numbers of people served also rose. Following is a census report of outpatient services for the fiscal year 1976-77:

1976-77 Outpatient Programs

Adult Day Treatment Center

Admissions	102
Census as of June 30, 1977	
Day Program	41
Evening Program	6
Patient Days	
Day Program	5,636
Evening Program	695

Adult Outpatient Services

Admissions	219
Individual Therapy Hours	5,163
Census as of June 30, 1977	121
Group Therapy Visits	2,213
Census as of June 30, 1977	32
Social Service Hours	291.5

Child and Adolescent Outpatient Service

Admissions	69
Census as of June 30, 1977	60
Therapy Hours	
Individual	1,644
Group	453
Social Service	1,377

The Bliss and LaVerne Forbush Children's Center

	Day School	After School
Children Enrolled	32	18
Percent of Family Members		
Participating in Therapy	89	52
Therapy Hours	967	184

Mt. Airy High School

All Students Enrolled	278
Maximum Enrollment	116
Minimum Enrollment	64
Student Class Hours	37,790
Enrollment as of June 30, 1977	76
Students Graduated	9
Students Completed Course Work But Received	
Diploma From Own School	1

COMDAP

Admission Interviews	153
Program Admitted To On Acceptance:	
Methadone Maintenance	34
Detoxification	24
Abstinence	39
Total	97
Evaluation for Baltimore District Court	196
Baltimore County Jail Detox Project	
Screened	113
Treated	105
Census as of June 30, 1977	133

NORCOM

Admissions	
Adult Program	443
Alcohol Program	176
Child Program	58
Cockeysville Satellite	55
Emergency Program	923
Total	1,655
Census as of June 30, 1977	
Adult Program	367
Alcohol Program	122
Child Program	30
Cockeysville Satellite	57
Emergency Program	119
Total	695

Direct Services Provided	Patient Sessions	Hours
Triage	810	303
Individual Therapy	7,681	5,961
Group Therapy	4,346	5,566
Family Therapy	352	341
Collateral	101	52

Consultative and Contractual Services

	Patient Visits
College Mental Health Services	941
East Baltimore Street Clinic	245
Greater Baltimore Medical Center	366

20. Completing the Modernization

AFTER MORE than a decade of new construction and renovation, 1977 marked the completion of the modernization of the original Hospital buildings. The fruits of this extensive work were greatly enhanced patient facilities, increased numbers of offices and improved support services. As a result of the renovation, 21 new beds were added to the adult services. The inpatient census remained consistently high throughout the year, ranging from 94% to 97% — a level of occupancy that pointed to the continuing need for the variety of inpatient services provided by Sheppard Pratt. Of the 680 patients admitted to the Hospital's various inpatient services, 555 were admitted to adult units (242 to the Short Term Treatment Unit, 70 to the Geriatric Unit, 59 to the Alcoholism Unit, with the remaining 184 patients going to general services), and 125 admitted into the medium to long term psychoeducational treatment program for children and adolescents. Based on the belief that regular interaction between the patient and therapist on a one-to-one basis is most desirable, the amount of individual psychotherapy provided patients was further expanded for all services.

That same year, the Trustees welcomed to the Board Mrs. Lois Hoffberger Blum. The first woman to be inducted to the Sheppard's Board of Trustees, Mrs. Blum was also a member of the Board of Trustees of Goucher College where she had pursued her undergraduate studies. A native Baltimorean, she received her degree as a mental health counselor from The Johns Hopkins Hospital and her masters degree in mental health from The Johns Hopkins University School of Medicine where, at the time of her induction, she served as Assistant in Psychiatry.

Another first during the year was the completion of the Community Needs Survey conducted by the Sheppard Pratt Development Advisory Council. Appointed several years earlier, the Council was comprised of a number of area residents "broadly reflective of the socio-economic characteristics" of the Baltimore metropolitan region. The group was invited to participate in Sheppard Pratt's long-term planning by advising on policy formulation and decisions dealing with those hospital programs delivering mental health care to the community. The Development Advisory Council was also asked to assist the Board of Trustees and the administration by identifying regional mental health needs and recommending future directions, priorities, and goals designed to meet those needs.

The Council recognized that in order to respond to these requests of the Board, an even broader base of community input and data was necessary. To this end the Council conducted a Community Needs Survey on the short and long term mental health needs of the community. The survey asked respondents to evaluate mental health services at Sheppard Pratt and in the community as a whole. Individual interviews with respondents focused on three general topics: 1, the participants' knowledge of what services were available; 2, the participants' opinion of the quality of services; and 3, the participants' perception of what services could be either improved or added to better respond to the community's needs.

The Council decided that open-ended interviews with only the general topics set in advance would be the best format for the survey. To facilitate and better direct these interviews, three-day seminars on interviewing techniques were attended by each of the volunteers who would conduct the study. When the Community Needs Survey was completed in 1977, over 300 mental health, government and community leaders had been interviewed. Twenty-

ABOVE: *Dr. Edward Senay speaks on "Substance Abuses" in November of 1980.*
LEFT: *Sheppard Pratt participates in City Hall's Noontime Lecture Series.*

one volunteers had donated 1,100 hours of their time.

With the results of the survey came both delight and disappointment. On the positive side, it was indeed heartening to see that the Hospital was already directing efforts towards nearly every area of need mentioned in the survey, which included (by percentage of citings by respondents) community centered services, 44%; sheltered living, 35%; preventive education, 32%; low fees, 21%; emergency services, 19%; residential treatment, 19%; and general psychological services, 17%. The staff and those concerned with the Hospital were also heartened to find that the community held Sheppard Pratt in extremely high regard in the mental health field, and that the findings of the survey were very closely aligned with the findings of the recently released President's Commission on Mental Health. Many of the same themes appeared in these two independently produced works: the need for public education; the spread of community based services; and the residual fear of mental illness. In trying to assess the needs of its own community, Sheppard Pratt had coincidentally touched on problems of national concern.

But there was also disappointment. Frustration with the Community Needs findings arose in two areas. First, it was upsetting to find that the public — even the public closely associated with the mental health field — was not fully aware of the services offered by Sheppard Pratt. Despite an active public relations program, the public was still unaware of the Hospital's many community based services, its educational programs and its innovative approaches to preventative mental health care. It was also disheartening to see that the public still held the misconception that Sheppard Pratt was a "rich person's hospital" with high fees.

It was remarkable to note that the public had no conception that, even from its very beginning, the Hospital had continuously cared for those who could not afford the cost of treatment. In 1977, when the Council's report was published, over 12% of Sheppard Pratt's inpatients and over 32% of the outpatients paid less than the cost of their treatment and 87% of all patient costs were paid by a third party (insurance, government grants, etc.). In his 1977 report, Comptroller Frederic F. Hinze noted that financial assistance for patients had reached a new peak, with 4.8% ($689,028) of all the Hospital's services being given on a charitable basis. Hinze also noted that in the past ten years growth in income had averaged 1.8% per year, while growth in the need for financial assistance had averaged 3.5% per year.

Sheppard Pratt's Comprehensive Drug Abuse Program, COMDAP, and its Northern Baltimore County Community Mental Health Center, NORCOM, for example, had required increasing funds in excess of what State grants and patients could cover. In 1977 Sheppard Pratt donated $168,000 to those two programs, whereas four years earlier only $16,000 had been necessary.

Marking the 125th Anniversary of the Hospital's original charter, 1978 was a landmark year for Sheppard Pratt. On May 28, 1853, the Maryland Senate had approved a charter to establish The Sheppard Asylum. And on May 28, 1978, Trustees, administrators, medical and support staffs of the Hospital joined together for a Service of Rededication to the principles of Moses Sheppard.

Anniversary Week activities included the Hospital's 15th Annual Scientific Day, a day-long symposium for Sheppard Pratt alumni and other professionals, highlighting reports and discussions on recent research, and a series of three public lectures on societal and mental health issues. Weekend festivities included an on-campus formal dance for patients, with entertainment provided by Zim

OPPOSITE: Dr. Gibson greets First Lady Rosalyn Carter at the American Psychiatric Association convention in Chicago in 1979.
LEFT: Staff Psychologist Dr. Benjamin Pope in 1979.
BELOW: Dr. Jeffrey Moss at a Staff lecture in 1980. Currently Moss is special program coordinator of the Hospital's Education Center; he lectures on the management of stress in the workplace, as well as on family life issues.

Zemarel and His Big Band.

The formal anniversary program was held on June 4, 1978 and included the ground-breaking for the new wing of the Chapman Building. This construction project began the final phase of the ten year program of modernization and improvement. The architectural firm of Cochran, Stephenson and Donkervoet worked closely with engineering consultant Fred W. Von Behren, Inc., to produce an energy efficient design that would lower operating costs of the new wing. The $6.5 million construction contract was awarded to Henry A. Lewis, Inc. To help fund the construction of the Chapman Building addition, the Hospital was able to float a $6.5 million tax-exempt bond through the Maryland Health and Higher Educational Facilities Authority. The interest rate for the bond issue was only 6.5%, making this an extremely important capital development. Since all previous Hospital loans had been at the prime rate, (15% at the time), this new bond issuance marked significant savings for the Hospital.

When completed, the new wing of the Chapman Building would house 96 child and adolescent beds, a full gymnasium, dining room, multiple purpose activity room, and a number of similar lounges and recreation rooms. With the addition of these facilities, the present Chapman Building would be modernized to provide extended facilities for the Forbush Center and Mt. Airy High School, headquarters for the Day/Evening Treatment Center, and offices for staff physicians.

At a time when government and state funding was declining on all levels, Sheppard Pratt's Annual Giving rose 40%; and time donated by volunteers was up 19%, equalling the cost of over 18 full-time employees. In addition, the Hospital Auxiliary held a flea market that raised $6,200. The 1978 annual appeal was coupled with a Capital Gifts Drive. Head-

ABOVE: *Three Presidents of the Board participating in the groundbreaking ceremonies for Chapman South in 1975, coincident with Sheppard Pratt's 125th Anniversary celebration. Left to right: Former President Bliss Forbush with the shovel, then-President John Luetkemeyer, current President W. Berkeley Mann, Dr. Gibson.*
OPPOSITE TOP: *John Luetkemeyer tries his hand with the groundbreaking shovel.*
OPPOSITE LEFT: *Guests listen to speakers at the celebration ceremonies.*

ed by chairman Douglas W. Kincaid, a recently elected member of the Board of Trustees, the "Heritage of Care" drive was one of the rare times that Sheppard Pratt appealed to the general public for such major financial support.

Along with the appointment of Kincaid to the Board, another important appointment during this anniversary year was that of Mrs. Henrietta G. Price as an Honorary Member of the medical staff. In 1924 she had succeeded Dr. William Rush Dunton, Jr., as director of Occupational Therapy. For the next 34 years, under her dynamic leadership, the Occupational Therapy Department expanded until 90% of the Hospital's patients benefited from her creative treatment. Mrs. Price wrote many articles for professional journals, spoke before professional gatherings and established an accredited school of occupational therapy. The impact of her work was so nationally and internationally extensive that the American Occupational Therapy Association preserved taped interviews with her in its archives.

Professional education, like that carried out by Mrs. Price, was always a part of the Hospital's committment to greater understanding and knowledge of mental health. Along with continuing education for currently practicing professionals, the Hospital's School of Mental Health Studies, begun in 1970, was constantly expanded to include a wider range of programs. In collaboration with neighboring colleges and universities, courses were designed for specific groups of mental health care providers. Yet, as community based mental health services expanded, it became more and more evident that education was needed not only for professionals, but just as importantly, for the general public.

"It is my firm conviction," said Gibson, "that we must assume a leadership role in preventative education for all sectors of our society, since a major answer to conquering mental illness is prevention. We must accelerate the development of programs that will teach people to understand emotional problems."

Gibson explained in his 1979 annual report, "If present and future generations are to be mentally healthy, they must learn to look upon depression and schizophrenia with the same positive attitude they look upon appendicitis or hypertension — as an illness that can be arrested and treated, an illness that carries no stigma or mystery." Thus, as an expression of the Hospital's commitment to community service and as an extension of its already far-reaching professional programs, Sheppard Pratt began a new phase of increased public education.

The new thrust towards public education had three primary goals. First, with education would come prevention. When people learned to spot the early signs of a mental problem either in themselves or others close to them, something could be done about it before a major and expensive step like hospitilization became necessary. Second, public education would serve to "de-mystify" mental health issues and prove psychiatry's value to "normal" people. And third, public education would benefit Sheppard Pratt directly by highlighting its strong reputation as a center of knowledge and excellent care, and by pointing out that the Hospital was accessible to the public and ready to help with many kinds of problems.

One of Sheppard Pratt's longest-established programs of public education was the offering of non-credit evening courses for adults. Many of these courses covered only one topic, such as "Techniques for Managing Child and Adolescent Problems and Behavior" or "Beyond Assertion: Strategic Skills in Communicating Self." The Hospital also conducted a weekly lecture series on current trends in mental health. During the 1978-79 academic year,

OPPOSITE: Dr. Melvin Sabshin gives the keynote address at the 125th Anniversary ceremonies in 1975. Medical Director of the American Psychiatric Association, Sabshin later became a member of Sheppard Pratt's Board of Trustees.
LEFT: Dr. Gibson on the phone.
BELOW: Dr. Gibson strolls the grounds of the Chapman South site, where the ground-breaking has just taken place.

lecture topics included: "Alchoholism — Its Occurrence and Treatment," "Drug Abuse — Its Occurrence and Prevalence," "Marriage and Divorce," "Depression in Everyday Life," "The Medical Consequences of Loneliness," "The Single Parent," and "A Death in the Family." There was a tuition charge for these courses, and although modest, Sheppard Pratt felt that the fee may have kept some people from attending. And so a series of free lectures was begun. These programs, which included such lectures as "Raising Emotionally Healthy Children," by child psychiatrist Richard A. Gardner MD; "Dying Persons, Their Families, and Us," by thanatologist Helene S. Goldberg; and "Agoraphobia," by Edward L. Ansel.

Another free series offered on a continuing basis was the Hospital's Alcohol Education Program, which met each Wednesday evening throughout the year. Designed to increase public awareness about alcohol use and abuse, the full series ran for nine weeks. Because each session was a self-contained unit, attendance could begin at any point and then continue for eight consecutive weeks — or one could attend just those lectures that he found most pertinent to his particular situation.

The Hospital and the Mental Health Association occasionally co-sponsored a Mental Health Fair on the Sheppard Pratt campus. At these times, Sheppard Pratt presented lectures and displays on subjects of interest to the general public and offered exhibit space to the area's mental health providers. On the occasion of the Hospital's 125th Anniversary, three free lectures were offered: "Mental Health and the Aging Process — Things You Wanted to Know about Growing Old and Were Afraid to Ask;" "Separated/Divorced? What It Is and What It Can Be;" and "Family and Marital Communications."

One of Sheppard Pratt's major educational thrusts

RIGHT: *Aaron Sopher looks at construction at Sheppard Pratt.*

came in programs for business and industry. This component of the public education effort was viewed as especially important. It was realized that the workplace had always been a fertile field for anxiety and stress. Thus, it was believed that managers with an understanding of psychological techniques could improve employee morale and productivity, as well as reduce their own tensions. With proper training in psychological techniques, managers would be in a position to identify employee mental health problems at an early stage and influence the person to seek help. With this in mind, beginning in 1977, the Hospital's Development Advisory Council and the School of Mental Health Studies co-sponsored a spring and fall seminar series for managers and administrators.

Each series included five or six programs directed towards the specific problems found in the workplace. Program topics included: "How to Recognize and Cope with Employee Problems — with a Major Emphasis on Depression;" "Women in Management;" "The Stress Response;" "The Use and Abuse of Chemical Substances by Those Who Work;" and "Family Problems Among Employees."

The 1979 fall series, introduced with a luncheon co-sponsored by the Greater Baltimore Committee, was attended by over 100 business and industrial leaders. Dr. Roy W. Menninger, President of the Menninger Foundation in Topeka, Kansas, spoke to the group on "Executive Stress." The programs on executive stress met with such gratifying response that it was decided to devote the major part of the 1979-80 effort to this single topic.

Sheppard Pratt also co-sponsored two programs with the Community College of Baltimore. The first, offered in the fall of '79, was a six-part free series on "Planning Your Future Retirement." The other jointly sponsored program with CCB was a continuing series of free noon-time lectures presented in the Board of Estimates Room of City Hall. This program, which focused on subjects of general interest such as effective communication, alcoholism, and depression, was a national "first." It was the first time a mayor of a major metropolitan city co-sponsored and supported a series of lectures on mental health issues — and held them in City Hall!

Another expression of the Hospital's educational programs was its Speakers Bureau. Given the high concentration of expert knowledge at Sheppard Pratt, it was only logical to organize a service offering guest speakers and discussion leaders to any organization interested in mental health issues.

Some of the lectures presented by the Speakers Bureau included: "Teenage Depression," at Catonsville Community College; "Grief and Loneliness," for a post marriage group; "Motivation and Stress," for the Environmental Management Association; and "Substance Abuse," for the Association of Personnel Managers.

The move towards increased public education was in no way limited to lectures and seminars. The Hospital began its own publishing venture with *The Catalyst,* a periodical written by mental health professionals for interested laymen and community leaders. The first issue in the winter of 1978 included articles entitled "Suicide," by Robert M. Brown, MA, a clinical psychologist at the University of Maryland's Institute of Psychiatry; "A Guide to Women in Management," by Diane M. Gibson, MS, Director of Activity Therapy at Sheppard Pratt; "Citizen Participation in Health Affairs: Who Needs It?," by Gerard J. Hunt, PhD, associate professor of sociology in psychology at the University of Maryland's Department of Psychiatry; and a reprint of Dr. Gibson's article "Private Psychiatric Hospitals: Excellence is Their Watchword," which originally

LEFT: *It's 1976, and construction for Chapman South is well underway.* **BELOW:** *The Auxiliary presents the Forbush School with computer equipment in 1983. Peg Taliaferro and Lucy Randolph (then President of the Auxiliary) look on as a youngster tries out his luck on a program.*

ABOVE: *The nurses' residence at Windy Brae as it appears today. In the early '80s a resident employee could get a room for only $25 per month!*
RIGHT: *Formerly the residence of the Hospital's formidable herd of dairy cows, the barn is now used as a maintenance building for the Hospital's innumerable pieces of furniture and equipment.*

ran in the July issue of the *American Journal of Psychiatry.*

During the time of this increased educational activity, in 1979 total inpatient admissions rose to 756 from 698 in fiscal year 1978. Of those admissions, 44.7% were male and 51.3% female. The median length of stay was 67.5 days for males and 51.1 days for female patients. Those staying longest were males 17 years and younger (median 313 days), while the shortest stays (median 29.9 days) were for females aged 26 to 44.

One of the Hospital's priorities at this time was the restructuring of the Department of Adult Psychiatry. Within the new organization the Hospital attempted "to reflect the interrelationship between the various adult inpatient and outpatient programs, and to facilitate the transfer of patients within the treatment system whenever possible." The Adult Admissions Office now served as the single point of entry for all adult services, which were grouped in two divisions: the Division of Adult Inpatient Programs, and the Division of Adult Ambulatory and Acute Inpatient Programs. The former provided treatment to those patients suffering from more serious mental disorders which require long-term intensive care, while the latter division included all outpatient programs and shorter-term and evaluative inpatient programs.

During the year, Wolfe N. Adler, MD, was named Director of the Division of Adult Inpatient Programs. Adler received his medical degree from the University of Maryland School of Medicine, served his internship at Sinai Hospital and completed his residency training in psychiatry at Sheppard Pratt. He joined the Hospital staff in 1966 and had, for the previous four years, served as its Director of Residency Training and Associate Director of the School of Mental Health Studies.

The new Director of Adult Ambulatory and Acute Inpatient Programs was Emile A. Bendit, MD. After receiving his medical degree from the University of Maryland School of Medicine, Bendit took his psychiatric residency training at The Henry Phipps Psychiatric Clinic of The Johns Hopkins Hospital. He had been a supervisor with the Mental Health Counselor Program of The Johns Hopkins University School of Medicine and an assistant professor in the Department of Psychiatry. Kent E. Robinson, MD, was named Director of Residency Training, replacing Adler in that post. Robinson, who had been with the Hospital since 1964, had also served as an assistant professor at the University of Maryland Medical College, and as Chief of Psychiatry at the Greater Baltimore Medical Center. Robinson had formerly been Director of Adult Outpatient Programs.

Receiving a new post as Medical Director of St. Albans Psychiatric Institute in Radnor, Virginia, Dr. Rolfe B. Finn resigned after 17 years at the Hospital. During his time at Sheppard Pratt, Finn served as Chief of Service, Director of Environmental Therapy, Associate Director of Inpatient Care, Director of Inpatient Services, and Director of Adult Inpatient Programs. In accepting his resignation, the Board of Trustees named Finn a permanent member of the Honorary Medical Staff.

To end the decade, Dr. Gibson began a two-year term as President of the Group for the Advancement of Psychiatry, Inc., an organization of approximately 200 American and Canadian psychiatrists selected for membership because of their capacity to generate ideas, work effectively in groups, and produce at a high level. Perhaps the most telling event of the 1970s, the presidency of this prestigious group served as an appropriate recognition of Gibson's leadership and direction of Sheppard Pratt in its inpatient, community service, and education programs.

21. Towards the Future

AS WITH ANY organization that has succesfully spanned the generations, the history of Sheppard Pratt has been one of change. And while evolution has been a characteristic of the Hospital since its founding, over the years there have been particular periods of *profound* change that have significantly altered the course of the institution. Entering the eighties, the Hospital found itself in one of those periods. During the seventies Sheppard Pratt expanded the interpretation of its mission to serve increasingly greater numbers of people. With the dawn of a new decade, in order to maintain these expanded services and the flexibility of patient care they provided, it was determined that corporate restructuring was necessary.

The Hospital, which had been governed by one all-encompassing Board of Trustees, is now divided into six separate corporations. The Sheppard and Enoch Pratt Health System, Inc. (SEPHS), an umbrella corporation, oversees the operations of five ancillary corporations. The first of the ancilliary corporations, The Sheppard and Enoch Pratt Hospital, Inc., was charged to "found and maintain an Asylum for the Insane; and to operate and maintain a hospital for the mentally ill." The Health System and Hospital corporations have the same Board of Trustees: W. Berkeley Mann (Chairman), Samuel Hopkins (Vice Chairman), John E. Motz, Dr. Philip Wagley, James D. Peacock, Dr. W. Byron Forbush, Paul R. Schlitz, Lois Blum-Feinblatt, Douglas Kincaid, Esther L. Cooperman, Dr. Melvin Sabshin, and John A. Luetkemeyer (Chairman Emeritus). To fulfill educational goals and objectives a second ancillary corporation, The Education Center of Sheppard-Pratt, Inc., was formed. The Sheppard Pratt Service Corporation and The Sheppard Pratt Investment Corporation, Inc., oversee physical operations and funds management, respectively.

When this corporate restructuring was finalized, the Sheppard Pratt Pysicians P.A. was formed. As was the procedure in most general hospitals, with the formation of this Professional Association, physicians' fees would now be charged as an entity separate from general hospital charges. This separation of fees deregulated a significant portion of the Hospital's current activities and thus removed them from the purview of the Health Services Cost Review Commission (HSCRC). This enables the Hospital to set and charge competitive rates without restrictive regulatory approvals. An additional benefit of the Physicians P. A. is that as the Hospital expands its services, it can do so without cumbersome fiscal controls.

Such benefits of the Physicians P. A. are just the beginning of the advantages found within the new corporate structure. With the new division of functions, those Hospital activities which in and of themselves could not be considered "health care" — such as education programs — are now outside the purview of the HSCRC and other regulatory agencies. Another advantage of the restructuring is a more clearly defined separation of funds for the various Hospital activities.

With each of the ancillary corporations forming its own Board of Trustees, under the new structure the Hospital is able to draw on the skills and abilities of a broader range of advisors. For example: a community leader with knowledge of investments who, because of time constraints or interests, may not be desirous of or willing to serve on an all-encompassing Board of Trustees with its monthly meetings is now able to direct his expertise towards one area of Hospital administration —investment.

These corporate level changes are accompanied by significant reorganization of the highest administrative levels. In May 1982 Dr. Gibson assumed

ABOVE: *"Creative Expressions" is part of the Sheppard's publications program for patients, and features examples of art and writing. One "Suzy K." did this impressive mask in 1984.*

ABOVE: *A 1985 aerial view of Sheppard Pratt. Windy Brae is in the upper left, the Casino in the upper right. The flat roofs on the New Central Building allow the viewer to easily distinguish it from older adjoining structures.*

ABOVE: *Baltimore's Mayor Schaefer presents Sheppard Pratt with an award for its City Hall Noontime Lecture Series in 1982. Left to right: Sylvia Nudler, Pat Mitchell, Priscilla Tainter, Morris Scherr, Mayor Schaefer, Dr. Gibson, Joe Culotta (Community College of Baltimore), Margaret Kraus.*
LEFT: *Dr. Gibson speaks at a mental health fair.*
TOP RIGHT: *How Aaron Sopher saw a staff lecture.*

the responsibilities of President and Chief Executive Officer of the Hospital. In this newly created position, Gibson was relieved of his day-to-day responsibilies for clinical programs. With these duties lifted, he is able to direct more time to the critical work required in planning the direction the Hospital will take in the future. Assuming the duties of Vice President/Medical Director was William L. Webb, Jr., MD. A nationally recognized clinician with experience in academic psychiatry, Webb's responsibilities at Sheppard Pratt included overseeing all clinical programs. One of his first duties was to recruit additional senior staff members.

Dr. Sheldon I. Miller, an expert in the field of addictions, was named Division Director of the Comprehensive Alcohol and Chemical Dependency Programs. Dr. Richard M. Sarles was named Director of the Division of Child and Adolescent Psychiatry. A child psychiatrist and pediatrician, Sarles has published widely on the topics of hypnosis with children, sexual abuse of children, and pediatric liaison. Accepting the post of Director of Nursing, Dr. Ann Marie Brooks came to the Hospital Sheppard with experience in administering a psychiatric unit in a large general hospital.

Along with these changes at the highest personnel level came changes on the Board of Trustees. Former State Senate Majority Leader and Director of the Office of Aging, Rosalie Abrams was inducted as a Trustee of The Sheppard Pratt Health Systems. After serving as a member of the Board for 30 years and as Chairman for the past 12 years, John A. Luetkemeyer was succeeded by W. Berkeley Mann. The eleventh Chairman of the Board, Mann became the ninth Quaker to hold this leadership position since Moses Sheppard founded the Hospital. Retaining the title of Past Chairman, Luetkemeyer said of his years as president, ''It has been my privilege to

LEFT: *Vocational testing is an important part of Sheppard Pratt's Occupational Therapy program, which increasingly outreaches into the Baltimore community. Here therapist Susan Athey explains a test.* **BELOW:** *Diane Hawkins gives instruction in leather-working, explaining how to color a hand-tooled belt.*

witness and to participate in a number of remarkable changes which have significantly altered the character of this institution. Sheppard Pratt has been transformed from an institution with a limited range of clinical programs —all of which were inpatient and half of which were custodial — into what we appropriately call today 'a comprehensive center for treatment, education and research.' ''

Step by step this transformation of the Hospital was accomplished only after painstaking analysis of the ever-changing environmental forces affecting the Hospital. Strategic planning was not merely an ideal but a necessity. Because Sheppard Pratt kept a constant watchful eye on the services it offered and those required by consumers — at a time when other private hospitals fell prey to buy outs by for-profit chains — the eighties found Sheppard Pratt financially secure. Under Gibson's leadership the Hospital was one of the first old-line private psychiatric hospitals to properly combine strategic planning and marketing.

Succinct as ever, Gibson explained this new approach: "Health care people have historically been provider-driven. The thought was, 'This is what we're trained to do; this is what we'll do.' But strategic planning and marketing dictate that hospitals must be consumer-driven. You must look at what people need. Once those needs are identified you examine which services you can best provide — without changing your mission. Then marketing, the last step in the process, is communicating those services to the right individuals — those who will most benefit from them.''

In recognition of the Hospital's strides in the areas of strategic planning and marketing, Sheppard Pratt was awarded the National Association of Private Psychiatric Hospital's (NAPPH) Gold Award in 1982 ''for total public relations programing.'' Presenting

the award to Dr. Gibson and Mrs. Priscilla Tainter of the Hospital's public relations department at the NAPPH Annual Meeting, Dr. Mark Gould, NAPPH President said, ''The (Sheppard Pratt) program projected the Hospital as a haven from the complex world; a place where growth and development is stressed and where people can receive help to live fuller and more satisfying lives. The Hospital effectively used brochures, advertising, media relations, and community education to achieve name recognition and referral development.''

But the new decade also brought its share of problems, most importantly in the form of severe cutbacks in coverage by certain third party payers. Those hardest hit by these reductions were patients in need of long term treatment. In response to these cutbacks, Sheppard Pratt worked to maximize the treatment possibilities of the 90-day coverage period. In 1982 the Hospital opened a Special Problems Unit. This intermediate treatment program, with a maximum stay of 90 days, was designed to address the restrictions imposed by the recent third party reductions.

A new Adolescent Short Term unit offered comprehensive diagnostic and intensive care. The unit quickly reached a full census, and along with providing needed short term services, was also helpful in identifying patients who needed longer term inpatient care. An Adult Intermediate Care Center with 42 beds was opened in July of 1984. This unit was designed to offer services to patients suffering from borderline disorders and eating disorders.

Along with added inpatient services the Hospital community outreach programs continued their expansion. In the early eighties the Sheppard instituted Counseline, a telephone tape library that allow callers to anonymously request and listen to tapes over the phone. The tapes range from more common help-line topics such as suicide and drug counseling

LEFT: *The Greenhouse is extremely popular with patients and visitors at the Hospital. Here volunteer Christy Shaw (appropriately wearing her "Plant Mom" apron) plants some seedlings.*
BELOW: *Greenhouse master Bruce Weaver gives his plants a drink.*

to help with self-confidence, marriage and family roles, and tension. At the end of each Counseline tape, callers are given a number to dial for further information on the subject. For many people, calling Counseline is the first step in seeking help for a serious problem; in its first year of operation Counseline received over 40,000 phone calls! This response — in conjunction with requests for Counseline brochures from health professionals, schools, churches, libraries, and businesses — demonstrated that once again the Hospital had brought to the community a much needed service.

In 1985 the Hospital's programs for professional and public education reached almost 15,000 persons with lectures, seminars, and workshops. "This kind of response," noted Mr. Mann, "demonstrates to us that the general public, health professionals and people in business have a desire and a need to understand more about the human issues addressed by these programs. It is our strong belief that training and education in these areas can help prevent many difficult personal problems."

With the success of these varied education programs, from humble beginnings in 1977 when 181 persons registered for a mere three programs, the Hospital's Division of Professional and Public Education had now grown beyond the present facilities of the Hospital. Studies to determine present and future needs of professional and public education were initiated.

Their findings demonstrated that Sheppard Pratt was regarded as a leader and a pioneer in the preventative health education area, and viewed as an organization of high quality with a professional and competent faculty. Results of the studies also proved that expansion and refinement of the Sheppard Pratt Education Program was mandated if the institution were to retain its vanguard role as a major compre-

hensive resource and learning center.

And most importantly, with the results of these studies came the idea of constructing an Education Center. As with Moses Sheppard's idea of founding an Asylum for the insane, little by little the Education Center became reality. Building concepts became architectural plans; initial fund raising efforts became gifts and donations from individuals and corporations. Today Sheppard Pratt finds itself ready to break ground on The Education Center of Sheppard Pratt, a National Center for Behavioral Studies.

To direct the efforts of The Education Center of Sheppard Pratt, a new Board of Trustees was formed. Members of The Education Center Board include: Edmund Cashman, Senior Executive Vice President of Legg Mason Wood Walker; Esther L. Cooperman; Hal Donofrio, president of Richardson, Myers & Donofrio; Richard Hook, President of the Bank of Maryland; Thomas Howell of Semmes, Bowen, and Semmes; Douglas Kincaid; John A. Luetkemeyer; W. Berkeley Mann; Dr. Melvin Sabshin, Medical Director of the American Psychiatric Association; Paul R. Schlitz; Dr. Edward N. Brandt, Jr., Chancellor of the University of Maryland, Baltimore County; and George McGowan, Baltimore Gas and Electric Co., President.

What Luetkemeyer termed as "the most visible symbol of a new era of change at Sheppard Pratt," the Education Center, designed by the architectural firm of Verkerke Boyles Linehan and Doyle, Inc., is a 38,000 square-foot building to be erected on the Hospital campus. Visitors will be received in a lobby and registration area that gives a fitting first impression of the Center's pleasing combination of spaciousness and light. Off the main lobby, a suite of executive conference rooms will host numerous educational gatherings. A 200-seat auditorium with

RIGHT: *Chapman South, looking north towards the Main Complex from the gymnasium doorway across the invariably crowded parking lot.*

front and rear projection facilities will be the scene of major lectures and symposia. Dining facilities, atriums, landscaped terraces, courtyards and walkways are all designed for the comfort of those participating in the education programs. Behind the scenes, another suite of rooms will provide faculty and staff offices, interview and counseling rooms, a board room, faculty lounge, and a computer center.

The building will house the Division of Professional and Public Education, which will be greatly expanded from its present capabilities. Under the leadership of Program Director, Irene Chesire, EdD, continuing education programs for health care professionals and human service providers; workshops for all levels of personnel in business, labor and government; as well as a variety of seminars, lectures, and personal development courses for individuals will all be offered. It is projected that within five years the annual registration for programs of the Professional and Public Education Division will be between 40,000 and 50,000.

For those participating in the Center's programs, as well as those unable to visit the Center, the Audio Visual Division will produce and market state of the art educational programs. Films, literature, audio and video cassettes and other materials will be produced in the Media and Production Center for national distribution. Many of these productions will be developed for organizations utilizing the offerings of the Contractual Services Division. This division of The Education Center will work directly with corporations, professional organizations and agencies (either at Sheppard Pratt, on-site at client headquarters, or at other designated locations) to provide specific training programs and consultation services. The Chesapeake & Potomac Telephone Co., McCormick & Co., the Maryland State Department of Education, and dozens of other organizations have already

benefitted from the services of this division.

Susan M. Hahn, MSW, directs The National Employee Assistance Resource (NEAR). This contractual employee assistance program seeks to identify, and if necessary, refer for treatment employees who exhibit health and personal problems that impact on their lives and their ability to perform on the job. Employees who cannot recognize their problems can be identified on the basis of impaired job performance and referred to the appropriate services. By preventing and solving the problems that are diluting employee efficiency, NEAR not only saves time and money, but jobs and lives as well.

Through appropriate mental health education, staff supervisors are trained to detect performance deterioration and to send the affected employee to NEAR. NEAR counselors evaluate the employee's needs and, if necessary, refer him to an extensive network of both counseling and treatment specialists. Through NEAR, employees are also provided with 24-hour emergency problem solving, follow-up services, and education programs. The W. R. Grace Co., Alexander and Alexander, Venable, Baetjer and Howard, and other large corporations have realized the wisdom of this program and have contracted NEAR to provide services to thousands of their employees.

Yet none of these programs offered by The Education Center, including the building of the Center itself, would be possible without extensive funding. Eight million dollars, roughly $5,000,000 for facilities and $3,000,000 for endowment and underwriting special programs, are needed. In efforts to raise these funds, the Hospital undertook its first general capital campaign in 131 years. Through the leadership of Capital Campaign Chairman Paul J. Scheel, President of USF&G, and Co-Chairmen George V. McGowan, President of Baltimore Gas &

Electric Co., and John Luetkemeyer, President Emeritus of Sheppard Pratt, the Capital Campaign Committee began the process of soliciting monies from corporations and individuals.

To further assist these fund raising efforts, the Hospital named Frederick J. Ramsay, PhD, as Director of Development. With over 20 years' experience in health professions education, planning and administration, Ramsay came to Sheppard Pratt from the University of Maryland at Baltimore where he was Associate Chancellor for Academic Affairs. In his new position, along with coordinating fund raising efforts, Ramsay serves as public information officer, Hospital liaison to legislative and other external bodies, and active participant in the Hospital's strategic planning.

In August 1984 Bob Gibson and John Luetkemeyer, along with Mayor William Donald Schaefer and Baltimore County Executive Donald P. Hutchinson, met with Governor Harry Hughes to request the creation of a bond issue for the purpose of constructing the Education Center.

In January 1985 State Senator John C. Coolahan and Delegate Robert Staab introduced to the legislature a $2.5 million bill on behalf of The Education Center of Sheppard Pratt, Inc. In his report to the Board of Trustees the following month, Gibson reported, "If there is any money available after the committees take their cuts from the Governor's askings, and the local committees carve out their needs, SEPH may be funded — best guess at this point — $1 million."

"Because of the highly competitive legislature at that time and the restricted availability of funds," Gibson now recalls, "If we'd gotten $500,000 I would have thought that incredible."

Discussions of the bill were heard in both the House and Senate during the first week of March.

It's the little things
That matter a lot.
It's finding love
Where there was not.
It's our love for them
And their love for us.
It's all of the warmth
And all of the trust.
It's so much an easier
Task to survive,
When we can find friends
To keep us alive.

Alan S. A4

ABOVE: *The architectural firm of Verkerke Boyles Linehan and Doyle, Inc., did this rendering for The Education Center, scheduled to break ground on June 10, 1986. By 1990 it is projected that annual enrollment for the Professional and Public Education Division will exceed 40,000.*
LEFT: *A 1985 Board meeting, presided over by (right to left) Dr. Gibson, John Luetkemeyer and W. Berkeley Mann (current President).*

On April 8, Sheppard Pratt received word that the State Legislature passed an Act to take effect June 1, 1985, creating a state debt in the amount of $2,000,000 for The Education Center of Sheppard Pratt. The Bill was passed unanimously in the House and with only five dissenting Senatorial votes. In his April report to the Board of Trustees Gibson noted, "The approval of our request is significant not only because of the monetary significance of the grant but because of the level of support it signifies for both Sheppard Pratt as an institution and The Education Center specifically." Support for The Education Center has come not only from government but from numerous corporations and individuals both within the State and nationally.

One hundred and thirty two years ago, Moses Sheppard said, "I desired to invest the estate in such a way as to meet some need that would not otherwise be met, and to see that the money would continue to be a blessing to men and women down through the ages." Today these same thoughts are reiterated by those who so freely give of both their time and monetary resources to create The Education Center of Sheppard Pratt.

"Sheppard Pratt has remained vital over the years," notes Gibson, "by its willingness to undergo again and again the changes required by a changing world. This has been accomplished by the persistent efforts and dedication of many people who understand that change is the only way to remain firm in an unchanging commitment to provide treatment, education and research."

Perhaps John Luetkemeyer best described this new era which the Hospital is about to enter when he said, "Much has been accomplished, and much remains to be done. This is how it will always be at Sheppard Pratt — our accomplishments will always point to new areas where we can do more."

BELOW: *The view everyone sees outbound from Sheppard Pratt — the back of the Gatehouse on Charles Street.*

Acknowledgements

THE EDITORS WOULD LIKE TO THANK:

Robert W. Gibson, MD, and his secretary **Chris,** for their willingness to schedule appointments at very short notice.

Diane Gibson, for her help in arranging sessions with the Occupational Therapy Staff.

Dr. Byron Forbush and his wife **Ann,** for proofreading galleys.

Marge Wisnom, for proofreading bluelines and fine-tuning minute details which might otherwise have escaped us.

Dr. Frederick Ramsay and **Duayne Trecker** of the Office of Development and Public Information, for their encouragement and help in the conceptualization and research for this volume.

Margaret Kraus of the Office of Development and Information, for her tireless help in sorting through the Sheppard's museum and archives.

Jay Harkey of French/Bray, our printers, for his patience throughout our numerous revisions, and his help in the presswork.